F...
ELEC...

Other Titles of Interest

FAULT FINDING
ELECTRONIC PROJECTS

by

R. A. PENFOLD

BERNARD BABANI (publishing) LTD
THE GRAMPIANS
SHEPHERDS BUSH ROAD
LONDON W6 7NF
ENGLAND

Please Note

Although every care has been taken with the production of this book to ensure that any projects, designs, modifications and/or programs, etc., contained herewith, operate in a correct and safe manner and also that any components specified are normally available in Great Britain, the Publishers do not accept responsibility in any way for the failure, including fault in design, of any project, design, modification or program to work correctly or to cause damage to any other equipment that it may be connected to or used in conjunction with, or in respect of any other damage or injury that may be so caused, nor do the Publishers accept responsibility in any way for the failure to obtain specified components.

Notice is also given that if equipment that is still under warranty is modified in any way or used or connected with home-built equipment then that warranty may be void.

© 1997 BERNARD BABANI (publishing) LTD

First Published – April 1997

British Library Cataloguing in Publication Data

A catalogue record for this book is available from the British Library

ISBN 0 85934 391 X

Cover designed by Gregor Arthur

Printed and bound in Great Britain by Cox & Wyman Ltd, Reading

Preface

Modern construction methods and improvements in components have greatly reduced the risk of newly constructed projects failing to work first time. They have also reduced the likelihood of faults developing in projects once they are "up and running." Home constructed electronic equipment, like the ready-made variety, tends to outlive its usefulness before it develops a fault. This is not to say that all electronic projects work first time, and that they will never go wrong. The occasional failure is inevitable. Usually the problem can be traced to a simple wiring error or something of this nature. However, there can be the very occasional "problem child" project, where everything seems to be just perfect apart from the fact that it does not work!

In a publication such as this it is obviously not possible to give individual servicing information for every electronic project ever published, or even for a small percentage of them. Fortunately, this is not really necessary, and by looking at the problem in a logical manner and proceeding accordingly it is possible to successfully fault find on practically any piece of electronic equipment.

The purpose of this book is to familiarise the reader with basic fault finding techniques which can then be applied to virtually any electronic project. Effective fault finding does sometimes require a certain amount of test equipment, but an inexpensive test meter is often all that is required. It can be helpful to have additional test equipment, and construction details for a few simple but useful items of test gear have been included in this book, together with details of their use. Little knowledge of electronics is assumed, and much of this publication will be of value to those who have limited experience of electronic project construction.

R. A. Penfold

Contents

Page

Chapter 1

MECHANICAL FAULTS

It must be well over thirty years since I built my first electronic project. In fact it was sufficiently long ago for this supposedly portable radio kit to be based on valved circuitry rather than transistors! There were, of course, no integrated circuits in those days, transistors were regarded as "new technology", and any semiconductor components were very expensive. My first radio project did work after a fashion, but was never particularly reliable. To some extent this was probably due to my poor quality workmanship, but some of the construction methods of those days were rather crude, as were some of the components. This sometimes made it difficult to produce a project that would work well, and go on working well for many years.

I must have built well over 1000 projects since my original effort, and most of them have worked well with good long term reliability. Things have changed a great deal over the last thirty years or so, and components are now generally more reliable and easy to use. Methods of construction have also improved, making it easier to get projects to work first time, and reducing the risk of a project developing a fault after you have managed to get it "up and running."

Unfortunately, improvements in components and construction methods cannot guarantee perfect results every time. The occasional project that fails to work first time is something that has to be regarded as an inevitability, as does the occasional failure of a project that has been working perfectly for some time. Some constructors regard a faulty project as a disaster, while others consider that this is where the real fun begins! Probably most constructors fall into the first category, especially if solving the problem proves to be long and difficult.

It is an unfortunate fact of life for the project builder that fault finding on some projects can be very time consuming. You may be lucky and spot the fault almost at once, but it may sometimes be necessary to make hundreds of checks before the

1

source of the problem is located. Once located, the fault is often found to be something quite simple, such as a crack in a printed circuit track, or a short circuit caused by a minute solder blob.

Prevention Better Than Cure

In my fairly considerable experience of fault finding on electronic projects, most of the faults are caused by what could generally be termed "mechanical" faults, such as broken leads, badly soldered joints, components fitted in the wrong places, accidental short circuits, and so on. Purely electronic faults, such as a "blown" semiconductor or a resistor that has gone high in value seem to be relatively rare, especially when dealing with newly constructed projects that have failed to work first time.

The lesson to be learnt from this is clear – prevention is better than cure. Most faults in newly constructed projects are the type of thing that could often be spotted with a little more vigilance during the construction process, or with a little checking before testing the newly constructed masterpiece. In theory we should all thoroughly check the wiring, etc., of every new project before we switch it on and test it. In reality we are often too impatient to do much testing, or any at all.

In most cases this will not cause any damage even if the project contains more than one fault, but the possibility of damage can not be totally ruled out. In the case of a mains powered project it would definitely be foolhardy to plug it in and switch on without making a few checks first. Apart from the risk of components being damaged due to wiring errors, the user could also be in danger. These days many projects are powered by quite large battery packs which can supply surprisingly high currents, and mistakes on a project of this type could result in smoke rising from some ex-parts! Even a humble PP3 battery can provide sufficiently high currents to damage delicate semiconductors. The less checking you undertake, the greater the risk of destroying components at switch-on.

It is best if projects are checked reasonably comprehensively as they are built. For example, once you have added a few components onto a circuit board, check that they are all in the right place and (where appropriate) fitted the right way round. It also pays to check that each component is in the right place

2

and round the right way just before it is soldered in place. This is particularly important with any multi-pin components that will be difficult to remove from the board once they have been soldered in place. Even with the aid of proper desoldering equipment, many multi-pin components are extremely difficult to remove from the circuit board. Doing so may well damage the component and (or) the circuit board.

It is important for beginners to check their projects very thoroughly. As constructors become more confident they generally do rather less checking on the final product, with most of the checking being done "on the fly" as the project is built. This is not necessarily a good idea, but it is understandable if constructors do less checking once they have gained some experience. They are less likely to make mistakes in the first place, and in most instances will spot most problems long before the project is finished. Beginners are more likely to make mistakes, will probably not spot most of them immediately, and have to rely more on checking the completed project.

An important point that is often overlooked is that any preset resistors must be set in accordance with any recommendations in the book or magazine article prior to switching on and testing the finished unit. In most cases failure to do any setting up prior to switch-on will not cause any damage, but the project may seem to be faulty when it is actually flawless. It is just that the preset resistors have totally the wrong settings and are preventing the project from functioning. With something like a class B audio power amplifier there is a real risk that a totally incorrect setting will result in a large quiescent current flow, possibly leading to the destruction of the output transistors. Therefore, always check this point before switching on, and check that any presets are given initial settings in accordance with the designer's instructions.

Many articles and books give the approximate current consumption of each circuit featured. If you own a multimeter, when initially testing battery powered projects it is worthwhile setting the multimeter to a suitable current range, and using it to measure the current consumption of the circuit. These days most projects have a negative earth rail, and the multimeter is therefore connected into the positive supply lead, as in Figure 1.1.

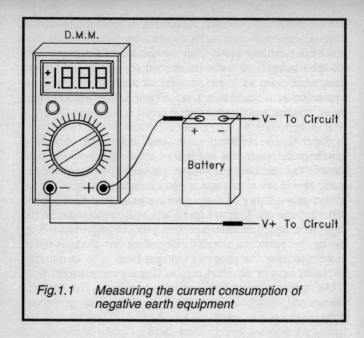

Fig.1.1 *Measuring the current consumption of negative earth equipment*

When measuring supply currents it has to be borne in mind that the current consumptions of some circuits vary quite considerably from one unit to another. There is no need to panic if the measured current consumption varies by 10 or 20% from the figure quoted in the book or magazine. In most cases a working project will not produce a current consumption that is within about 10% of the typical current drain figure. Large errors of around plus and minus 50% or more are more dubious, and probably indicate that there is a problem. However, ever deviations as large as this do not always indicate a problem.

The main advantage of monitoring the current drain of the circuit is that it will be immediately apparent if the current drain is very high. You can then switch off at once, hopefully before any serious damage has occurred to any of the components. Do not be too hasty to switch off a project that has a high initial current consumption. Most projects consume an initial burst of current as the electrolytic capacitors in the

4

circuit charge up. However, this burst of high current should last no more than about half a second or so. Some circuits seem to have a relatively low or high current for a few seconds after switch-on, but then settle down to the normal level. This is presumably due to it taking a few seconds for some of the capacitors in the circuit to take up their normal working voltages, and for the circuit to settle down at its normal working voltages.

Even if a multimeter is not used to monitor the current consumption, there may be signs of an excessive current drain. Apart from the obvious ones of rising smoke and exploding components, you may notice the characteristic smell of hot components! This may simply be due to a power device in the circuit that is designed to operate at a high temperature, and the book or article will normally warn you if a component in the project will become heated in normal operation. If in doubt, always switch off at once and thoroughly recheck the unit. It is probably as well to do this even if the project seems to be working properly. If components are overheating, something is wrong and the project is unlikely to go on working for very long.

On The Fly

When checking projects as you construct them, what sort of problems should you look out for? In the main you simply have to look for obvious errors, such as a component fitted in the wrong position, or a short circuit between two tracks of a printed circuit board due to excess solder. To a large extent it is a matter of "keeping your eyes peeled", and carefully checking that each component is correctly positioned before you actually solder it in place.

Most short circuits caused by solder blobs or splashes will be fairly obvious, and there is no excuse for not spotting them as they occur. From time to time there may be the odd minute piece of solder that bridges two tracks, and which is difficult to see. It is a good idea to make a careful visual inspection of the board after completing a lot of soldered joints within a small area of the board. This usually means in the vicinity of d.i.l. integrated circuits or other d.i.l. components. However, joints can be packed closely together in other parts of the board, such as where there are banks of diodes or resistors. Printed circuit boards seem to become ever more intricate, which gives an ever greater risk of accidental short circuits.

Modern components are very reliable, and "duds" are virtually unknown these days. At one time there was a problem with so called "genuine duds." These were substandard or even totally non-functioning transistors and diodes that were marked to look like the "real thing", and sold as such. This practice seemed to die out many years ago, presumably because the bulk prices of most semiconductors became so low that there was no point in producing forgeries of them. Recently this practice has resurfaced, but only some up-market integrated circuits seem to have been forged. In particular, some "dud" memory chips and microprocessors have come to light. There is no problem of this kind with the components used in most electronic projects. Provided you buy new components from a reputable supplier, there is very little chance of you being supplied with a faulty component.

The fact that components are in perfect working order immediately after they are manufactured does not mean that they will still be in that condition once they have been soldered into your project. Obviously there is a risk of physical damage occurring at some stage, such as when they are on their way to you in the post. It is not a good idea to use any component that shows any obvious signs of damage, unless the problem is clearly just a surface blemish.

Obviously something like a few bent pins on an integrated circuit can soon be bent back into place, but be more wary of something like a chip in the casing of a resistor or a capacitor. The damage might be superficial, but physical damage to a resistor can result in its value being significantly altered. For a capacitor it is more likely that a short circuit between the two metal plates will be produced due to the dielectric being pierced. Damage of this type renders a capacitor totally unusable.

If you have suitable test gear there will be no difficulty in testing any suspect components. If the value of a component is within its tolerance limits, it should be perfectly usable. Obviously most beginners do not have the test gear needed to check resistors, capacitors, etc., and it is then a matter of

6

"playing safe." Any component which shows any signs of serious damage should be replaced.

It is probably when components are being fitted to the circuit board that they are most at risk. Modern components are mostly quite heat resistant, but this does not mean it is impossible to overheat them when they are being soldered into circuit. Probably most electronic components will be destroyed if you take too long when soldering them in place. Completing a small soldered joint should take no more than a second or two, and applying the bit of the iron for this length of time should not produce any damage. Keep the soldering iron in place for a few seconds though, and a damaged component is the likely outcome. In an extreme case you might find that the circuit board also suffers, with the copper pad coming unglued from the board.

Passive components such as resistors, capacitors, and small inductors may well show obvious outward signs of damage if they are overheated. This will usually be in the form of discolouration, with the body of the component probably darkening. Also, the component may become much more shiny or dull, depending on the type of covering.

The fact that a component shows clear signs of being overheated does not mean that it has become useless. Its value might still be well within its tolerance rating, and the component might still be perfectly usable. On the other hand, a significant shift in value is quite likely (especially with resistors), and overheating a component is likely to significantly impair its reliability. An overheated capacitor will often be rendered totally useless. If a passive component is overheated it makes sense to take no chances and replace it. After all, most passive components cost very little these days, and it is unlikely to cost much to replace the occasional suspect component.

Some capacitors can be damaged by overheating, but with little outward sign of any problem. It is mainly the box style polyester capacitors which have no outer casing that give problems, but it has been known to occur with other types. The early open construction polyester capacitors were notoriously unreliable, with only a very small amount of force being needed to rip the leads away from the body of most components. Modern types are much tougher, but are not totally immune to

7

this problem.

These days the more likely cause of trouble is a leadout wire becoming detached while the capacitor is being soldered into place. The problem seems to be caused by outward pressure on the leadout wires, perhaps because the hole spacing of the board does not precisely match the lead spacing of the capacitor. When the first leadout wire is soldered to the board, the heat from the iron travels up the leadout wire and effectively desolders it from the body of the component. Although you might reasonably expect the detached leadout wire to be self evident, in many cases it is very difficult to spot. The leadout wire is often left firmly soldered in position on the board, and apparently still attached to the capacitor.

Even with the aid of a magnifier it can be virtually impossible to see the gap between the leadout wire and the body of the capacitor. This type of problem is most easily located by holding the body of the capacitor and gently twisting it. If the component twists out of place it is broken! Polyester capacitors having plastic casings are now readily available, and I tend to use the cased type whenever possible. I have never experienced any problems with detached leadout wires when using cased polyester capacitors.

Semiconductors are the components that are most easily damaged by heat, and it makes sense to take extra care when dealing with these. I always fit d.i.l. devices in holders, which totally eliminates any risk of damage due to overheating. Transistors can be fitted in holders, but this is not really necessary. Provided you complete each soldered joint reasonably swiftly it is unlikely that transistors and diodes will come to any harm. Extra care is needed when dealing with germanium devices, which are far more vulnerable to heat damage that normal silicon types. Most germanium semiconductors are now obsolete, and are unlikely to be used in new designs.

The only exception are germanium diodes such as the ever popular OA90 and OA91. These have characteristics which make them superior to silicon diodes in certain applications, and it seems likely that they will remain in use for many years to come. Some constructors use a heat-shunt on each lead of a germanium diode as it is soldered into place. I have never found this to be essential, but each soldered joint should be

8

completed as quickly as possible. It should preferably take no more than a second or so to complete each joint. Germanium diodes should be the last components to be fitted to the board.

Charged Up

Many modern semiconductors are vulnerable to damage from static charges. Virtually any semiconductor device can be "zapped" if it is subjected to a sudden static discharge, and all semiconductors should be kept well away from any obvious source of static electricity. This includes television sets, computer monitors, virtually anything made from plastic, and possibly even your cat or dog! The semiconductors that are most at risk are the MOS (metal oxide silicon, or metal oxide semiconductor) variety. Many modern semiconductors are in this category, including single and dual gate MOSFET transistors, CMOS logic integrated circuits, most computer peripheral chips, certain operational amplifiers such as the CA3130E and CA3140E, and most of the more complex integrated circuits currently available.

There are numerous precautions that can be taken when dealing with static sensitive devices, and a vast array of antistatic equipment can be obtained. These include such things as conductive workbenches, and even cages that are designed to keep out static charges. Much of this equipment is expensive and is not really intended for use by hobbyists. It is aimed at electronics professionals, for use either in laboratories or on production lines. Unless you want to impress your friends, there is little point in buying equipment that would cost several times as much as the total cost of the components it would protect during its lifetime!

Some electronic hobbyists tend to go to the opposite extreme and treat MOS devices just like any other semiconductors. In truth, you would probably get away with it for the vast majority of the time if you adopted this approach, but it is still not something that I could recommend. Some MOS semiconductors are quite expensive, and not taking due care to protect them from static charges would have to be regarded as somewhat foolhardy. There is obviously less financial risk with devices that cost just a matter of pence, but there is potentially a great deal of trouble in locating and replacing components

9

that have been accidentally "zapped." I would strongly recommend that at least a few basic precautions are taken when dealing with MOS devices.

The most important of the basic precautions is to use a holder for all MOS semiconductors unless the project designer specifically states that a component must be soldered direct to the circuit board. This is not normally necessary, but direct connection can be essential in some specialist applications, particularly where very high frequencies are involved. If direct connection is required, always use a low leakage soldering iron which has an earthed bit. If the iron's mains cable includes an earth lead, the bit of the iron is almost certainly earthed. If the iron has a two way cable, its bit is obviously not earthed, and it should not be used with MOS devices. When using holders, do not fit the components into their holders until the circuit board and any wiring to off-board components have been finished.

MOS semiconductors are normally supplied in some form of anti-static packaging. The most common forms of packing are conductive foam, blister packs having a metal foil covering over cardboard backing, and plastic tubes. The idea of the first two is to effectively short circuit all the pins or leadout wires together so that a high voltage can not build up across any of them. Remember that it is a high voltage difference between terminals that causes damage, and not a high voltage per se. Apparently, the idea of the plastic tubes is to insulate the components within from high voltage charges. However, some of these tubes now seem to be made from a conductive material, and they presumably operate by shorting the terminals together.

Whatever form the anti-static packing takes, always leave the components inside the packing until you are ready to plug them into their holders. Some advocate plugging the components into place without touching any of the pins or leads. This might be possible with transistors, but is not normally feasible with integrated circuits. The problem with integrated circuits is that their pins are usually splayed outwards slightly (Figure 1.2(a)), and they must be bent inwards before they will fit into a holder (Figure 1.2(b)). It is difficult to do this without touching the pins, unless you obtain the clever little gadget which can instantly "straighten" the pins of any normal d.i.l. integrated

10

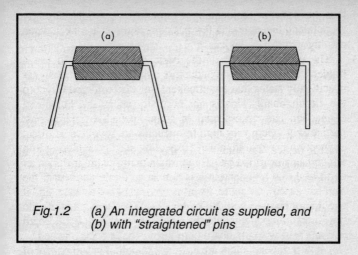

Fig.1.2   (a) An integrated circuit as supplied, and
           (b) with "straightened" pins

circuit. However, do try to touch the pins as little as possible.

For an amateur it is not worth going to the expense of special anti-static workbenches, but you might like to invest in one of the conductive mats which can be used on any worktop. In use the mat is earthed, as are any static charges in its vicinity. However, it seems to be perfectly adequate if you simply avoid having any obvious sources of static electricity anywhere near the work area. For example, do not build projects close to television sets or computer monitors. Also, avoid wearing clothes that are known to be static generators, or work in a room which has a carpet that is known to occasionally send the sparks flying. In general, it is materials having a very high plastic content that give problems, while man-made materials or a mixture of the two are largely static-free.

Some constructors touch something that is earthed before they start work on a circuit board. This should remove any charge within your body, and greatly reduce the risk of "zapping" any sensitive components. Clearly, something like stroking a cat or dog just before you start work on your latest project would not be a good idea, particularly if you know your pet is known to be a "highly charged" type!

It is perhaps worth pointing out again that it is not only MOS semiconductors that are prone to damage from high static

11

voltages. MOS semiconductors are most at risk as they can be damaged by a gradual build-up of static electricity. Eventually the voltage becomes so high that it causes the gate insulation to break down, damaging the semiconductor structure in the process. This does not happen with other types of semiconductor as they provide much lower resistance paths, which results in any charge being leaked away too rapidly for any build-up to occur. However, the introduction of a large static charge can result in it rapidly discharging through an ordinary semiconductor device, "zapping" it in the process. Consequently, all semiconductors should be kept well away from any potential sources of large static discharges.

Buckling Under

Using integrated circuit holders should avoid problems with "zapped" semiconductors, and holders make it easy to correct matters if you inadvertently get an integrated circuit fitted the wrong way round. They are not entirely free of problems though, and they can cause occasional difficulties. One problem is simply that certain types of holder do not seem to grip the integrated circuits very reliably, and as fast as you plug devices into place, the holders "spit" them out again. Fortunately, the vast majority of modern holders do not suffer from this problem, but always make quite sure that the integrated circuits are fully pushed down into place. This should ensure that they stay in place.

Some holders have surprisingly short pins which hardly protrude on the underside of the board. When using this type of holder it is essential to make sure that the holder is fully pushed down onto the board before making any of the connections. It must also be kept firmly held in place while the connections are made. In fact it is always important to ensure that d.i.l. holders are fully pushed home, and that both rows of pins penetrate as far as possible through the board while the connections are made. With any pins not protruding at least a millimetre or two through the board there is a risk that the solder will simply cover over the end of a pin without actually making an electrical connection to it. There may be no outward sign of anything wrong, and this is a fault that will only be brought to light by some electrical testing.

When fitting integrated circuits into holders it is all too easy to get one or two of the pins buckled. This occurs because the offending pins are fractionally misaligned. In most cases where this happens it will be obvious that all is not well. The pin bends outwards and is clearly visible, or the integrated circuit will simply not push right down into the holder. You can then remove the integrated circuit, carefully straighten the bent pins, and try again. You need to be very careful when straightening the pins of integrated circuits as it is easy to break off some of the pins. I find that the best way is to carefully flatten out each pin with the aid of a small screwdriver blade and my thumbnail.

If a pin should break off, all is not necessarily lost. Provided there is still at least a small piece of the pin left protruding from the case (which there usually will be), a piece of wire can be soldered to this, and used as a make-shift pin. The wire needs to be about 22 s.w.g. (0.71 millimetres in diameter) tinned copper wire. Soldering a tiny piece of wire to the stump of the pin is virtually impossible, so start with a piece about 50 millimetres or more in length. Solder one end to the remains of the pin, making the connection as quickly as possible. Then trim the wire to length and bend it into place so that lines up as accurately as possible with the other pins. It should then be possible to fit the device into its holder, although it is obviously essential to take extra care when fitting the device in place. With luck, this will give the desired result, and will usually provide good long term reliability.

On very rare occasions one or two pins buckle inwards, and there may be no outward signs of anything wrong. This depends on the type of holder used, but it can be difficult to detect this problem if the integrated circuit appears to be properly "seated" in its holder. In fact it can only be detected by electronic testing. With some types of holder it is possible for one or more pins to fit into the holder in slightly the wrong place. Everything appears to be all right, but some of the pins are actually failing to make contact with the pins of the holder. Once again, this is something that can only be detected by electronic testing. If a project fails to work, and a check of all the wiring, etc., fails to bring any problems to light, it is probably worthwhile removing all the integrated circuits to make sure that there are no buckled pins or similar problems.

When removing a d.i.l. integrated circuit, do not do so by grabbing it with your fingers and pulling. This may seem quite reasonable, but in practice it almost always results in one end of the device pulling free of the holder while the other either lags behind, or simply remains in the holder. The result is a lot of buckled and bent pins, possibly with one or two broken off. Various integrated circuit extraction tools are available, and these are mostly in the form of outsize tweezers with hooked ends that fit under the integrated circuit. Any of these should enable even the largest of d.i.l. devices to be removed intact. Alternatively, there is usually no difficulty in removing a d.i.l. device with the aid of a small screwdriver. Simply prise the device slightly free at one end, and then repeat this procedure at the other end. If the screwdriver is then returned to the first end of the device once again, there should be no difficulty in prising the device completely free of the holder.

Board Stiff

No matter how carefully you construct a project, and regardless of the amount of checking you do during construction, I suppose that the occasional failure is inevitable. Whether you resort to test equipment at an early stage or undertake further visual checking first depends on individual circumstances. Comprehensively checking through a circuit board, component by component, and joint by joint, is probably not something most people would regard as the height of fun. In fact it can become quite tedious if you have a large board to contend with. For the more experienced constructor armed with a fair range of test gear it is probably best to resort to electronic testing at an early stage, after perhaps giving the project a quick visual check in search of any obvious errors that had previously been overlooked. Electronic testing is covered in detail in chapter two, and is not something we will pursue further here.

Beginners are not exactly "spoilt for choice", and will probably lack the necessary equipment and know-how to undertake electronic testing. This leaves no choice but to use more basic methods of checking. Looking on the bright side, most newly constructed projects that fail to work have a fairly obvious fault, such as a wrongly fitted component or a "dry" joint. As already pointed out, it is highly unlikely that you will besupplied with a faulty component. If you get everything in the project wired-up and connected correctly, it will work.

If the worst comes to the worst, and your latest masterpiece fails to work, just where do you start in the fault finding process? To a large extent it is just a matter of looking for the kind of error that you check for during construction. Probably the most frequent sources of errors are accidental short circuits on the circuit board, and mistakes in the hard wiring. I always start by looking for short circuits on the underside of the circuit board. Although it might seem that a solder "blob" or trail would be easy to spot, the causes of accidental short circuits are often very difficult to see. One reason for this is that they are often very small. Another is that they can be covered by remnants of the flux in the solder.

Even if you have very good short distance eyesight it is still advisable to use a magnifier of some kind to provide a larger and clearer view of the board. I normally use an 8X loupe (also known as a "lupe") obtained from a photographic shop. This only enables a small amount of the board to be examined at any one time, but it gives a really detailed view of things. Many constructors prefer to use an ordinary magnifying glass, which gives a less detailed view of the board, but permits a larger area to be viewed at any one time. Either way, you will not see very much if the board is heavily contaminated with burnt flux. There are various flux cleaners available, but I have never found it necessary to resort to one of these. Scrubbing the board with an old toothbrush, or any similar type of brush, seems to remove the flux very quickly and thoroughly.

It is important to work your way methodically across the board, making quite sure that no areas are left unexamined. "Sod's Law" dictates that if you leave even a small area of the board unchecked, that is the area where the fault will lie! Pay particular attention to any parts of the board where the connections are packed particularly densely. In the case of stripboard, also pay special attention to the ends of the copper strips, and to places where there are breaks in the strips. It seems to be easier to produce solder bridges between two joints at the ends of tracks or near breaks in the strips. Any solder bridges that are found can be easily removed onto the hot bit of a soldering iron, or can be carefully cut away using a sharp modelling knife.

Blade Runner

I have not found a visual inspection, even a close one with the aid of a magnifier, to be a one hundred percent reliable method of locating solder bridges. Some years ago when I was constructing large numbers of projects on stripboard panels, I was plagued with solder bridges that proved to be difficult to locate. I found that the easiest solution was to score between each pair of strips a few times using a sharp modelling knife. Obviously it is essential to take due care with anything such as this, but it proved to be very effective provided the blade of the knife was taken along the full length of each set of strips.

If you have access to some form of continuity tester, this can be used to check for short circuits between copper strips. It can also be used to check that any breaks in the copper strips of a stripboard panel have been produced correctly. It has not happened to me very often, but I have had a few projects that failed to work because a break in a strip had not been implemented properly, with a piece of copper track a fraction of a millimetre wide being left intact. A piece of track this narrow will still provide quite a low resistance connection, but it can be virtually impossible to see even with the aid of a loupe.

A continuity tester simply indicates whether or not there is a short circuit between its two test prods, and it does not need to be anything particularly elaborate. Most multimeters have a built-in continuity tester, or can effectively act as one if set to a resistance range. A proper continuity checker setting is better, as this normally provides a "beep" sound if there is continuity between the test prods. This enables checks to be made without having to keep looking away from the test prods. This may seem like a minor point, but the test prods tend to slip out of position each time you look away from them, making it difficult to make large numbers of checks in rapid succession.

Hidden Enemy

A do-it-yourself continuity tester project can act as a useful introduction to the hobby, and is useful once it has been built. I would strongly urge using a type of tester that can distinguish between a true short circuit and a forward biased semiconductor junction. Most modern circuits are liberally scattered with semiconductor junctions, which provide what are effectively a large number of diodes interconnecting various parts of the circuit. These diodes do not simply occur where there are actual diodes in the circuit, but can be found wherever there is practically any type of semiconductor device. For example, with no power applied, a transistor is effectively two diodes, as in Figure 1.3. Note that continuity checking should always be undertaken with the power switched off, and in the case of a mains powered project it should also be disconnected from the mains supply.

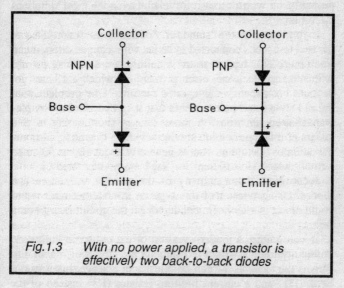

Fig.1.3   With no power applied, a transistor is effectively two back-to-back diodes

When reverse biased the diode junctions are of no consequence, since they provide a very high resistance. When forward biased they provide quite a low resistance, and can "fool" the more simple forms of tester. The built-in continuity tester function of most multimeters operate at a very low voltage which is inadequate to bias a silicon junction into conduction. Consequently, they will not respond to semiconductor junctions. If you use a multimeter set to a resistance range, with both analogue and digital meters the voltage drop through the

17

silicon junction will produce a resistance reading that is well above zero, as should any low resistances in the circuit.

Seeing The Light

Very basic continuity testers are generally "fooled" by semiconductor junctions, as are their users! With many circuit boards this seems to result in continuity being indicated between virtually every pair of tracks, rendering the testing process a complete waste of time. Unless you have a tester that can properly differentiate between a genuine low resistance path and a forward biased semiconductor junction it is probably not worth using it for testing even the most simple of circuit boards.

In days gone-by the "standard" continuity tester consisted of the two test prods connected in series with a large battery and a torch bulb. This type of tester is definitely not suitable for use with modern electronic circuits, many of which are based on delicate but expensive integrated circuits. One problem with the old style torch bulb tester is that it can be "fooled" by forward biased junctions. A more serious shortcoming is that testers of this type operate at relatively high operating currents. Torch bulbs operate at what is generally about 100 to 500 milliamps, which is sufficient to "zap" many integrated circuits, and can even damage many of the smaller transistors and diodes. Using a tester of this type on a modern circuit board could result in every semiconductor on the circuit board being destroyed!

If you require a modern version of the old torch bulb style continuity tester I would recommend the circuit of Figure 1.4. This is the same as a torch bulb tester in essence, but it uses a l.e.d. (D1) and a current limiting resistor (R1) instead of the torch bulb. This circuit operates with a l.e.d. current of only about three milliamps or so, which is sufficient to give good brightness from a high efficiency l.e.d. Ideally D1 should be a type which is intended for operation at currents as low as a couple of milliamps. The three volt battery can be two AA (HP7) size batteries in a plastic holder.

Since the tester can supply a maximum potential of just three volts, and a maximum current of just over three milliamps, there is no risk of it damaging any of the components in the

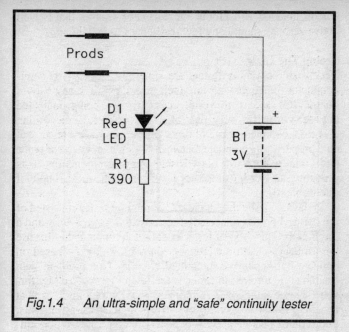

Prods

D1
Red
LED

R1
390

B1
3V

+

−

Fig.1.4   An ultra-simple and "safe" continuity tester

circuit under test. Strictly speaking it does not have the ability
to ignore forward biased silicon junctions, but in practice the
l.e.d. current will be reduced to less than half the normal level
with a forward biased junction across the test prods. This obviously gives much reduced brightness from the l.e.d., and the
user should realise that there is not true continuity across the
test points.

Sound Testing
The circuit diagram of Figure 1.5 is for a continuity tester that
provides an audible tone when activated, and ignores diode
junctions. In fact it is a three-state tester which gives no tone if
there is no continuity, a low frequency tone if there is a very
low resistance across the test prods, and a higher pitched tone
if there is a somewhat higher resistance or a single forward
biased diode junction. A highly detailed description of this circuit would be out of place here, but a brief description will be
provided.

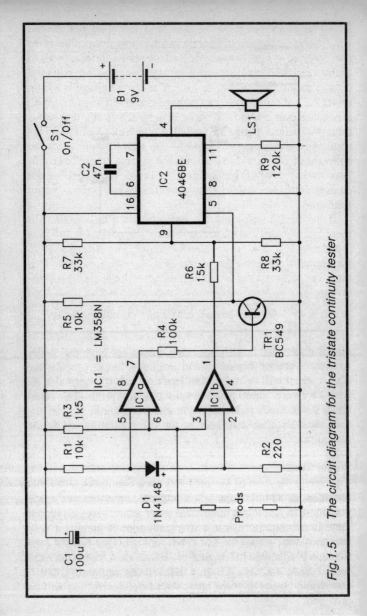

Fig.1.5   The circuit diagram for the tristate continuity tester

20

IC1 is at the heart of the unit, and this dual operational amplifier is connected to operate as a window discriminator. In other words, it detects when the voltage across the test prods is within certain limits. These limits are set by the potential divider formed by R1, D1, and R2. The lower voltage is a little under 0.2 volts, and the upper voltage is about 0.85 volts. With a resistance of around 30 ohms or less across the test prods there will be less than 0.2 volts fed to pins 6 and 3 of IC1. This results in the output of IC1a going high, which in turn sends the collector of TR1 low and activates the voltage controlled oscillator based on IC2. The output of IC1b goes low, pulling the control voltage to IC2 to a low level, and giving a low output frequency.

If the resistance across the test prods is a little higher, or there is a forward biased junction here, the voltage fed to pins 3 and 6 of IC1 falls within the "window". The output of IC1a then remains high, but the output of IC1b now goes high. This takes the control input of IC2 to a higher voltage giving a higher tone from LS1. With the test prods open circuit, or a high resistance across them, the voltage fed to pins 3 and 6 of IC1 is higher than the maximum "window" voltage. This results in the output of IC1a going low, which results in IC2 being switched off. The circuit therefore gives the required action, with a low frequency tone being produced with a very low resistance across the prods, a higher tone with a medium resistance or forward biased junction across the prods, and no tone being emitted under other conditions.

A suitable stripboard layout for the continuity tester is provided in Figure 1.6 (component side view) and Figure 1.7 (copper side view). Construction of this project is very straightforward, and should not overtax even complete beginners. Note that IC2 is a CMOS device, and that the usual anti-static handling precautions should therefore be observed when dealing with this component. IC1 must be a dual operational amplifier that is suitable for single supply operation. Most of the more common types (LM358N, LF353, TL082CP, etc.) are not suitable for use in this circuit. The CA3240E should work well, but note that this has a MOS input stage, and that it requires the usual handling precautions.

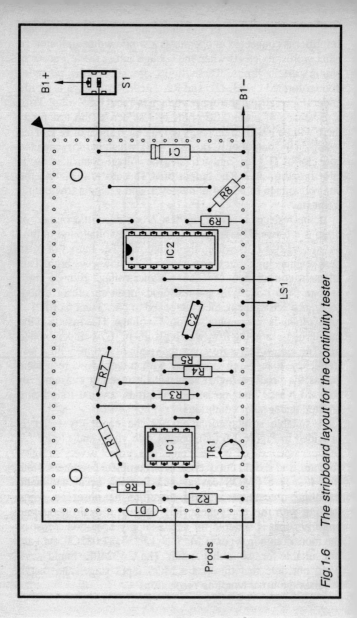

Fig. 1.6   The stripboard layout for the continuity tester

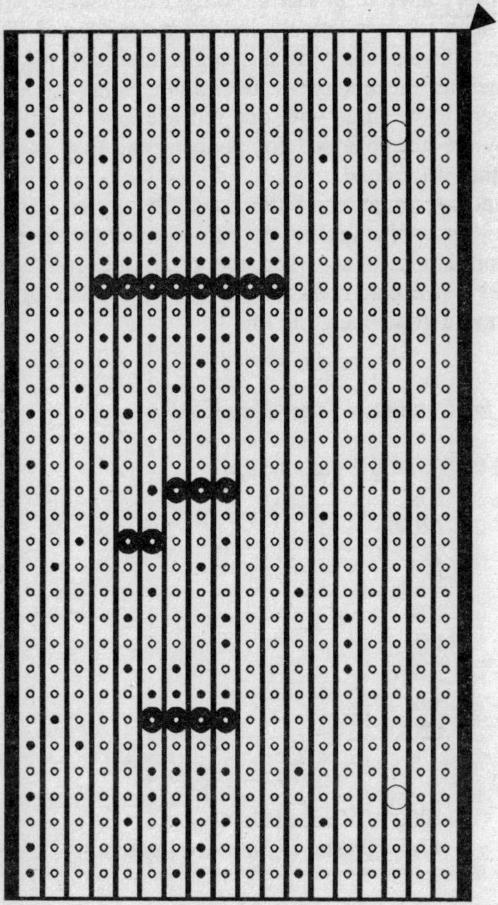

Fig.1.7   The underside of the continuity tester board

23

LS1 is not a normal moving coil loudspeaker, and the circuit has insufficient drive to operate even a sensitive high impedance loudspeaker. It must be a ceramic resonator, and virtually any type should operate well in this circuit where a high volume level is not required. In fact the output frequencies have deliberately been made relatively low in order to give low efficiency from the resonator. In this application high volume levels are neither necessary or desirable. Some ceramic resonators seem to be fitted with one red lead and one black lead, but they are not polarised components, and they can be connected either way round.

The current consumption of the continuity tester is only about three to four milliamps, but the consumption increases to around 10 milliamps or so when the prods are connected together. A PP3 size battery is adequate to power the circuit and should have a good operating life.

Components for Continuity Tester (Fig.1.5)

Resistors (all 0.25 watt 5% carbon film)
R1	10k
R2	220R
R3	1k5
R4	100k
R5	10k
R6	15k
R7	33k
R8	33k
R9	120k

Capacitors
C1	100μ 10V radial elect
C2	47n polyester (7.5mm lead spacing)

Semiconductors
IC1	LM358N
IC2	4046BE
TR1	BC549
D1	1N4148

Miscellaneous

S1	SPST min toggle switch
LS1	Cased ceramic resonator
B1	9 volt (PP3 size)

Small plastic box, 0.1 inch matrix stripboard having 33 holes by 18 copper strips, battery connector, test prods, 8-pin d.i.l. i.c. holder, 16-pin d.i.l. i.c. holder, wire, solder, etc.

In Use

Whatever type of continuity tester you use, the first stage is to check each pair of adjacent tracks to determine whether or not there is a short circuit between them. When dealing with projects constructed on stripboard it is as well to bear in mind that there are often a lot of link-wires on the board, and that adjacent copper strips are sometimes meant to be connected together. Look on the component side of the board to check for intentional links before spending a lot of time using a magnifier in search of non-existent solder bridges! With stripboards you can also use the continuity tester to ensure that any breaks in the copper strips have been completed successfully. Simply connect one test prod to each side of the break being checked. A short circuit indicates a fault, and it should be possible to cure the problem by further cutting of the strip.

As a last resort, a continuity tester can be used to check that each lead and pin on the top side of the board is connected to the appropriate copper track on the underside of the board. This is often the only sure test for a "dry" joint, but I would recommend a thorough visual inspection of the underside of the board first, as this will often reveal any problems of this type. The "driest" joint of all is the one you forget to solder, and this is something we all do occasionally. Even a quick visual check should reveal any missing joints.

Also look for joints which are very flat, with little or no sign of a pin or leadout wire poking through the joint. If a component is not fully pushed down onto the board there may be no electrical contact between the lead or pin and the solder. A mechanical bond is sometimes provided by excess flux, which gives the impression that a strong and usable joint has been produced, even though no electrical contact is provided. A continuity tester will show whether or not there is a proper electrical joint.

"Dry" joints often look wrong in appearance, and it makes sense to check any joints of this type first, before working methodically across the board. A bad joint is often surrounded

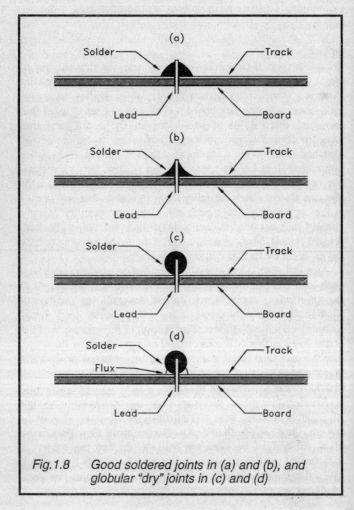

Fig. 1.8   Good soldered joints in (a) and (b), and
globular "dry" joints in (c) and (d)

26

by a black mess, which is mainly half burnt flux from the solder. Even if the underside of the board has been cleaned, there are often tell-tale signs if any "dry" joints are present. A normal joint is usually quite shiny in appearance, with the solder having a normal bright metallic appearance. The solder in "dry" joints often has a cracked and crazed surface, and a very dull appearance. Also, a good soldered joint has a sort of mountain shape, as in Figures 1.8(a) and (b).

A "dry" joint usually has a more globular appearance, and the shape is often slightly irregular, as in Figures 1.8(c) and (d). A joint of the type shown in Figure 1.8(c) is usually fairly obvious, as the solder has obviously failed to flow over the copper track. The joint is mechanically weak, with the lead and solder both free to move around to some extent. Things are less obvious with a joint of the type depicted in Figure 1.8(d) because some excess flux fills the gap between the blob of solder and the copper track. This gives a joint which might be mechanically quite strong, but the flux insulates the lead from the copper track. If a joint looks at all suspect, a quick test with a continuity tester will soon show whether or not it is providing a good electrical connection.

Modern solders are very good, and there will be a reason if a bad joint has been produced. Assuming that you have not simply used too little solder, or some other unsound soldering method, it is likely that corrosion or grease on one of the surfaces is causing the problem. Before resoldering a joint you should always clean both surfaces by scraping them with the small blade of a penknife. There should then be no difficulty in producing a good quality joint the second time around.

Hard Wiring
The hard wiring of many projects is aptly named, since this aspect of construction is often more tricky than fitting the components onto the circuit board. The obvious first step when checking this wiring is to compare the wiring with the wiring diagram, one lead at a time, to ensure that all the leads are present and correct. Getting a couple of leads crossed over is easier than you might think, particularly with a project that has a large amount of point-to-point wiring.

27

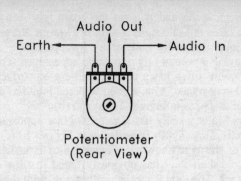

*Fig.1.9   Correct method of connection for a
           potentiometer used as a volume control*

Doing so will not invariably result in the complete failure of
a project, but it can usually be relied upon to at least provide
some rather odd results. For example, a volume control might
have a rather odd control characteristic, or even work in reverse
(i.e. clockwise rotation giving a reduction in volume). If a
project almost works, but the controls are in some way a bit
erratic, it is advisable to check the wiring to the offending
controls sooner rather than later.

If a volume control or other potentiometer control works
"backwards", the track connections have been transposed. In
other words, the connections to the two outer tags have been
swapped-over. The more common error with volume controls
is for the "top" and wiper connections to be swapped over. This
gives something that approximates to the right action, but with
an odd control characteristic. Also, at low volume control
settings there may be a fair amount of distortion on the audio
output signal. A volume control connected in this fashion
operates by placing an increasing load on the output of the
preceding stage as the volume is reduced. At low volume
settings the control is virtually placing a short circuit on the
output of the previous stage! It is this that results in the

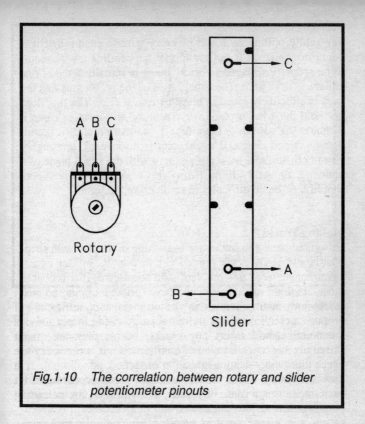

Fig.1.10 *The correlation between rotary and slider potentiometer pinouts*

increased distortion at low volume settings.

Figure 1.9 shows the correct method of connection for a rotary potentiometer when it is used as a volume control. Slider potentiometers seem to be rather out of fashion these days, and are little used in projects for the home constructor. The range of slider potentiometers currently available seems to be rather limited, but they are still used in a few projects (notably audio mixer projects). With slider potentiometers the obvious method of connection is the wrong one. The middle tag connects to one end of the track and not, as one might expect, to the wiper. Figure 1.10 shows the correlation between the tags of rotary and slider potentiometers.

Pull The Other One

Try gently pulling each end of every wire to ensure that it is connected reliably. It can sometimes happen that a wire seems to be properly soldered in place, but it is actually fixed at one end by a "dry" joint. The usual cause of the problem is that the wire is effectively glued in place by excess flux. The flux does not hold the wire in place very securely, and in most cases it insulates the wire from the pin or tag so that no electrical connection is completed. If a bad joint is discovered, thoroughly clean both surfaces by scraping them with the small blade of a penknife, or gently filing them with a miniature file. There should then be no difficulty in resoldering the joint.

Making Tracks

Unwanted breaks in tracks are something of a rarity with stripboards and ready-made printed circuit boards. In fact I have never encountered this problem with stripboard. It is probably most common with home produced printed circuit boards, where only a tiny scratch in the etch resist is sufficient to produce a crack in one or more tracks. A visual inspection of the board should reveal any breaks, but as they are often extremely narrow (a fraction of a millimetre), it is necessary to check thoroughly using a magnifier of some kind.

Alternatively, check for a short circuit between the ends of each track using a continuity tester. Many printed circuit tracks branch out in various directions, and in such cases it is necessary to check for continuity between any end point and every other end point of the track. Once a break has been detected, a visual inspection of the track should soon reveal the exact position of the break.

In theory there should be no problem in simply soldering over the break with a small blob of solder. In reality it is easy to accidentally bridge quite large gaps, but is often difficult to deliberately solder over quite narrow cracks. If the blob of solder fails to bridge the gap it will usually be quite obvious. There will be two distinct mounds of solder on either side of the break. Even if the blob does seem to bridge the gap properly I would still recommend checking that all is well using a continuity tester.

30

With any awkward track breaks the answer is to solder a small piece of wire across the break. Trying to solder a few millimetres of wire in place is virtually impossible, so start with a longer piece (about 50 millimetres or more). Tin one end of the wire, and the copper track on either side of the break. There should then be no difficulty in soldering the tinned end of the wire across the break. Finally, the excess wire is cut away using a pair of wire clippers.

Colour Codes

Anyone who has pursued the hobby of electronics over the last thirty years or so could hardly fail to notice the ever diminishing size of electronic components. Modern "bog standard" resistors are tiny compared to their equivalents in the 1960s. In most respects this reduced size is an advantage, but one slight drawback is that it makes it more difficult to read the colour codes. This can be a major problem for those who have below average eyesight, and I also find that some resistor codes are difficult to read under certain types of artificial light. For example, with some resistors red, brown, and orange bands are easily mistaken under tungsten lighting. If you have trouble reading the colours of the bands in resistor codes, try looking at the components through a magnifier. Even using a fairly low power type should make things much more clear.

Many modern resistors have five band colour codes instead of the traditional four band variety. Unfortunately, there are two different types of five band coding. It is obviously necessary to take care when dealing with the five band colour codes, as there is a slight risk of muddling the two types and coming up with the wrong value. If in doubt I simply measure the values using a multimeter. If possible, avoid having a spares box which contains resistors having two or three different styles of colour coding.

Summary

Prevention is better than cure. Check and double check everything at each step of construction.

Observe basic anti-static handling precautions when dealing

with MOS devices, and keep all semiconductors away from large static charges.

If a project fails to work, switch off immediately and recheck all the wiring, etc. Keeping a faulty project switched on might result in damage to some of the components.

Probably the most common cause of problems, particularly amongst beginners, is "dry" joints. Look carefully at the soldered joints, and try again with any that look suspect.

Mistakes in the hard wiring are easily made, so always check this wiring very carefully, especially if any of the controls act in an odd fashion.

Look for short circuits on the copper side of the circuit board using some form of magnifier. Problems with solder blobs and splashes are very common with stripboard, so this is one of the first things you should check if a stripboard project fails to work.

It is much easier to find solder blobs, etc., if the underside of the board is cleaned with a small brush, such as an old tooth-brush.

Tests with a continuity tester are helpful at finding awkward short circuits between tracks, cracks in copper tracks, bad joints, etc. Some form of continuity tester should be regarded as an essential "tool of the trade."

Ideally the continuity tester should be one that is not "fooled" by forward biased semiconductor junctions.

Look for signs of physical damage to components, and replace any that have sustained anything more than the most superficial damage.

Remember that if you get everything connected together in the right fashion, the project will work (honest).

Chapter 2

LINEAR CIRCUITS

If checks for mechanical faults fail to show up the problem with a newly constructed project, electronic testing should soon reveal the source of the problem. If a fault develops in a project that has been working properly for some time, it is worthwhile giving it at least a cursory check for signs of mechanical damage, but it is probably best to resort to electronic testing at an early stage. The most likely cause of the problem is a "blown" component, but there may be no outward signs of the problem. Electronic testing is probably the only way that this type of fault can be located, unless you are prepared replace each component, one-by-one, until the project works.

The obvious drawback of electronic fault finding is that it requires some test equipment and a certain amount of technical knowledge. Fortunately, a great deal of testing can be undertaken using nothing more than a multi-range test meter ("multimeter"). A multimeter can provide a great deal of information about how well (or otherwise) each section of a linear circuit is functioning. Logic circuits are very different to linear types, and need largely different methods of testing. Consequently, these two types of circuit will be considered separately. In this chapter we will consider fault finding on linear circuits, such as amplifiers, filters, radio receivers, and power supplies. Testing logic circuits is covered in Chapter 3.

Danger

There is a slight problem with voltage checks in that they can only be taken with power applied to the circuit under test. Applying power to a faulty circuit is a bit risky, and could result in damage to some of the components. It is advisable to start by checking the current consumption of the circuit to ensure that it is not vastly too high. The text of the book or article containing the design should give the approximate current consumption for the circuit. Assuming the measured current consumption is no more than about 50% or so higher than the typical figure, there should be no problems if the circuit is left switched on for long periods.

Maintaining power to the circuit is not a good idea if the measured current consumption is many times higher than the expected figure. The only exception would be if the circuit should have a very low current consumption. If a circuit consumed 10 milliamps instead of one milliamp, for example, the current and power consumptions of the circuit would still not be very high, and there would be little or no risk of any damage occurring. If a circuit consumes (say) 500 milliamps instead of 100 milliamps, that is a very different matter, and it would be advisable to switch off immediately. Methods of dealing with circuits that consume high currents are covered later in this chapter.

Now You See It ...

The circuit diagrams for some projects show typical voltages at strategic points in the circuit, but this is relatively rare. In most cases you will need to look at the circuit and estimate the voltages present. Whether you base your tests on marked voltages or estimates, it is important to bear in mind the affect the multimeter has on the circuit under test. The point to bear in mind is that the multimeter taps off some current from the test circuit, and that this alters the test voltages. The multimeter is effectively a resistor which is added into the circuit across the test points. The higher the value of this resistance, the smaller the affect of the multimeter on the test voltages.

Analogue multimeters tend to have relatively low resistances. The sensitivity of an analogue multimeter is normally expressed as so many kilohms per volt. This figure is normally between 1k and 20k per volt. The reason for using this method, rather than simply stating a resistance for the meter, is that the resistance changes from one voltage range to the next. An analogue multimeter set to d.c. voltage measurement has a circuit of the type shown in Figure 2.1. Each voltage range uses a different resistor in series with the meter. The higher the voltage range, the higher the value of the series resistor.

The most common sensitivity for an analogue multimeter is 20k/volt, and a multimeter of this sensitivity is based on a 50 microamp meter. It therefore taps off up to 50 microamps from

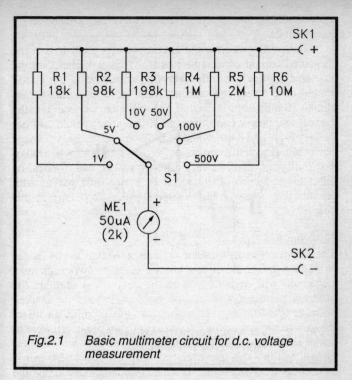

Fig.2.1   Basic multimeter circuit for d.c. voltage measurement

the circuit under test. When set to (say) the 10 volt d.c. range, a 20k/volt multimeter has a resistance of 200k (20k × 10 = 200k). This is not significant when measuring the voltage from a low impedance source, such as the output of an amplifier, but it can be very significant when measuring the voltage produced by something like a high resistance bias circuit. The circuit of Figure 2.2 helps to illustrate the problem. Here we have an operational amplifier used as a high input impedance buffer stage. The two bias resistors (R1 and R2) have a high value of 1M each in order to give the circuit a high input impedance. The input impedance is actually equal to the parallel resistance of R1 and R2, or 500k in other words.

Measuring the voltage at the junction of R1 and R2 using a 20k/volt multimeter switched to the 10 volt range gives an erroneous result. R1 and R2 provide a bias level of half the

35

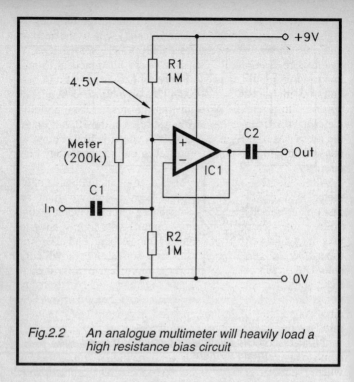

Fig.2.2   An analogue multimeter will heavily load a high resistance bias circuit

supply potential, which in this case means that a bias level of 5 volts is produced. Connecting the multimeter across R2 to measure the bias level effectively places a 200k resistor in parallel with R2. This effectively shunts the value of R2 from one megohm down to 167k ((1000k x 200k) divided by (1000k + 200k) = 167k). This results in a reading of under two volts instead of a reading of around 5 volts.

This problem is not due to a fault in the multimeter, and the reading of under 2 volts correctly reflects the voltage present when the multimeter is connected to the circuit. It is erroneous in that a potential of about 5 volts is normally present at the test point, and it is only when the multimeter is connected to the circuit that the lower voltage is produced. As soon as the multimeter is disconnected from the circuit the voltage returns to its normal level.

It is clearly advantageous to use a multimeter that has as high a sensitivity as possible. Unfortunately, due to the need to make the meter movement reasonably tough, sensitivities of much more than about 20k per volt are not practical. Some inexpensive multimeters have sensitivities as low as 1k per volt. Any multimeter is a lot better than no multimeter at all, but you need to be careful when interpreting results from a multimeter having a sensitivity as low as this. On the 10 volt range the meter has a resistance of just 10k, which is low enough to considerably load down readings taken on practically any bias circuit.

Although the relatively low resistance of an analogue multimeter is a definite drawback, it does not make such an instrument unusable on high impedance circuits. When taking voltage readings on low current circuits you simply have to take the loading effects of the meter into account, and allow for them when interpreting results. This is something we will consider later in this chapter. With very low current circuits an analogue multimeter, especially a low sensitivity type, is probably not going to tell you anything particularly helpful. However, circuits operating at currents of a few microamps are relatively rare, and this is not too great a drawback.

On the face of it, the low resistance problem can be overcome to some extent by always using the higher voltage ranges where the meter exhibits higher resistances. The problem with this is that low voltages measured on a high voltage range give very little deflection of the meter, and in practice are hard to read accurately. Another point to bear in mind is that the accuracies of analogue multimeters are generally expressed as a percentage of the full scale value. Thus, although a multimeter might have an error of no more than plus or minus one percent at its full scale reading, the error could be as large as plus and minus ten percent at one tenth of the full scale value. In order to obtain really good accuracy it is essential to take each reading on a range where the measured voltage represents about thirty percent or more of the full scale value.

Digital Alternative
Digital multimeters largely avoid the need to make adjustments to expected readings when making measurements on low

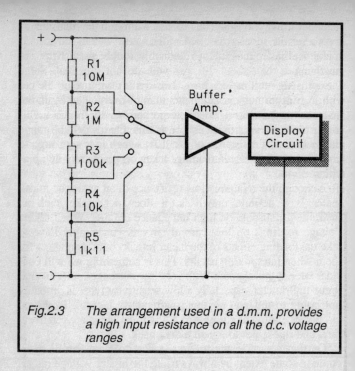

*Fig.2.3   The arrangement used in a d.m.m. provides
a high input resistance on all the d.c. voltage
ranges*

current bias circuits. An analogue multimeter is a passive
circuit which relies on current from the test circuit to drive the
meter. A digital multimeter (d.m.m.) is an active circuit which
has an amplifier at the input, and this provides an extremely
high resistance on all the d.c. measuring ranges. Unlike an
analogue instrument, a digital multimeter does not operate on
the basis of series resistors plus a current measuring circuit.
Instead it consists of a sensitive voltage measuring circuit having a very high input resistance, plus a simple attenuator.
Figure 2.3 shows this general arrangement.

In practice the basic voltmeter circuit usually has a full scale
sensitivity of 0.1999 volts or 1.999 volts. The attenuator provides additional measuring ranges at 19.99 volts, 199.9 volts,
and 1999 volts. Most instruments are not actually usable up to
the full 1999 volts on the highest range, and can only be used
safely up to about 600 volts. This is more than adequate for

general testing purposes. The resistance through the multimeter is equal to the series resistance of the attenuator resistors, and in practical instruments this is almost invariably about 10 or 11 megohms.

Such a high resistance obviously helps to minimise problems with loading of the test circuits, and is only equalled by most analogue instruments when they are set to their highest d.c. voltage range. The resistance through the meter can not be completely ignored though, and can still affect readings significantly when very low current circuits are being tested. Applying a typical digital multimeter to our previous example, we have the effective circuit of Figure 2.4.

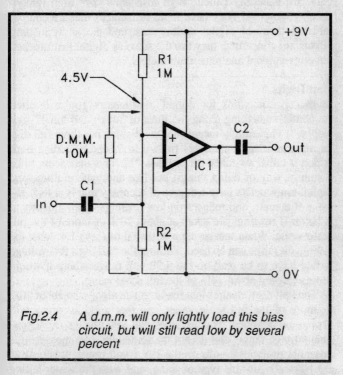

Fig.2.4   *A d.m.m. will only lightly load this bias circuit, but will still read low by several percent*

The resistance through the multimeter is very much higher than the value of R2, but it still effectively reduces the value of

39

R2 from 1M to just over 900k. This is still a reduction of almost 10%, which will be reflected in a noticeably reduced voltage reading. The bias resistors for a very high input impedance buffer stage could be several megohms each, which would result in even heavier loading of the test point. A digital multimeter largely avoids loading effects, but you still need to "keep your eyes peeled" for the occasional awkward circuit that could give problems.

It should perhaps be pointed out that there are analogue instruments which use an amplifier ahead of the meter circuit, giving the instrument characteristics that are more like those of a digital multimeter than a conventional analogue type. These units are generally called "high resistance" or "high impedance" voltmeters. They have input resistances that are comparable to those of digital multimeters, and as far as loading effects are concerned, they are the same as digital instruments, not conventional analogue multimeters.

Half Digits

In the specifications for digital multimeters you will often encounter something along the lines of "three and a half digit display". This simply means that the display has three full digits that can display numbers from 0 to 9, and a leading digit which is either switched off or reads "1". This may seem to be a strange way of doing things, but like analogue multimeters, digital multimeters have a degree of accuracy that is at its highest at full scale, and reduces on low readings. Consequently, it is better if readings are taken at about 20% or more of the full scale value. When measuring a potential of (say) 1.4 volts, the 1.999 volt range can be used. Without the half digit this voltage would have to be read on the 9.99 volt range where it would represent only about 14% of the full scale value.

The half digit ensures that readings can always be about 20% or more of the full scale value, and that good accuracy will always be obtained. This assumes that you always use a suitable voltage range, and do not try something like measuring a potential of about 2 volts on the 199.9 volt range. It is easy to inadvertently do this type of thing, and with the meter telling you that there is (say) 2.2 volts at the test point it all seems quite plausible. With some multimeters you may actually be getting quite accurate readings, but with others such low readings are very inaccurate. It is best to err on the side of caution and ensure that all readings are taken on an appropriate measuring range.

Spoiled For Choice

I am often asked to express an opinion as to which is the best type of multimeter for the hobbyist, a digital or an analogue type. At one time digital instruments were quite expensive, and economic factors meant that most hobbyists had to opt for the analogue variety. These days the difference in cost is relatively small, and some good low cost digital instruments are available. If you are working on a tight budget, then an inexpensive analogue multimeter might be the only type that falls within your price range. These often have quite low sensitivities of around 1k or 2k per volt, together with a limited number of d.c./a.c. voltage, d.c. current, and resistance ranges. Even a basic instrument of this type is extremely useful and will permit a large range of tests to be made, but there can be large loading effects to take into account when making d.c. voltage measurements.

If you can afford it, the small extra cost of a cheap 20k per volt analogue multimeter or an inexpensive digital instrument is fully justified. I have tended to prefer analogue instruments in the past, but I was "brought up" on multimeters of this type. They do have one or two advantages, such as what is generally a wider bandwidth when used to measure a.c. voltage. Most digital multimeters are only suitable for use with low frequency a.c. signals, such as 50Hz or 60Hz mains supplies. They fail to work at frequencies of more than about 500 hertz, which makes them unsuitable for measuring even a 1kHz test signal, let alone test signals at high audio frequencies. Analogue multimeters seem to operate well over the full 20Hz to 20kHz audio range, and often work with reasonable accuracy at frequencies well beyond 20kHz.

Another advantage of an analogue multimeter is that a slowly varying voltage, such as one caused by low frequency feedback, will clearly show up as such. A digital instrument will give a series of fluctuating readings, but it is not normally possible to see from these exactly what is happening at the test point. The voltage is clearly unstable, but the exact nature of the problem is left unclear.

Digital multimeters certainly have their advantages, and for most users these easily outweigh any slight drawbacks. One advantage is simply that they are generally more accurate. Analogue multimeters often have accuracy figures that are inferior to those of the average digital instrument, but most meter movements can not be read with a high degree of precision anyway. Analogue multimeters usually have quite large meters, often with a mirrored arc mixed in with the scales. This mirrored arc helps the user to avoid parallax errors.

Even so, most analogue multimeters have a reading accuracy that is roughly equivalent to a two, or possibly two and a half digit display. This compares with a three or four and a half digit display on most digital multimeters. Of course, in practice the added accuracy of a digital multimeter is not necessarily a great asset, since it is often only approximate voltage readings that are needed. However, it can be useful when testing something like a precision resistor having a tolerance of one percent or better. Also, when good accuracy is needed it is much quicker and easier to read a digital display than an analogue type.

Shocking Truth

An obvious advantage of a digital instrument is that it has a very high input resistance which largely obviates the need to allow for loading effects when making d.c. voltage measurements. Another considerable advantage is that digital multimeters are generally tougher than the analogue variety. The problem with analogue instruments is the delicacy of the moving coil meter movement. In order to obtain good sensitivity it is necessary to use a lightweight meter movement which is vulnerable to physical vibration and shocks.

If you knock a digital multimeter off the workbench a few times it may sustain a few cracks to its plastic casing, but in all probability it will work as well as it ever did. Do the same thing with an analogue multimeter and you are likely to have problems with poor accuracy or the meter "sticking", if it works at all. If you opt for an analogue multimeter it is essential to give it the "kid gloves" treatment if you want it to go on working well for many years.

All the digital multimeters I have used were able to accept a d.c. input voltage of either polarity, and this now seems to be a fully standardised feature of digital multimeters. If you connect the meter with the wrong polarity, the display adds a minus sign ahead of the voltage reading to indicate that the input voltage is a negative type. If you get the polarity of an analogue multimeter wrong, the pointer is deflected in the reverse direction, and hits the end stop. This is unlikely to do any damage, but will clearly not do the meter movement a great deal of good either! Repeatedly making this mistake is likely to gradually degrade the performance of the meter movement.

Apart from avoiding possible problems with damage to the meter, the bipolar nature of digital multimeters makes them much more convenient when making measurements on circuits which have dual balanced power supplies. Many audio circuits and circuits which utilize operational amplifiers fall into this category. With a digital multimeter the negative test prod is connected to the central 0 volt (earth) supply rail, and voltage readings are then taken relative to this. The multimeter's display shows whether readings are positive or negative. This approach is not possible with an analogue multimeter, and the normal solution is to measure voltages relative to the negative supply rail. This is a perfectly practical solution, but is not as convenient as measuring voltages relative to the earth rail.

Both analogue and digital multimeters often have some useful "extras" included in the specification. These include such things as a continuity checker setting with a built-in buzzer, transistor checkers, capacitance ranges, and frequency ranges. These are all very useful, and well worth having. Fortunately, even some of the lower cost instruments offer an amazing variety of features and measuring ranges, so it is not necessary to spend a fortune in order to get an "all singing, all dancing" multimeter. However, it is mainly the digital instruments which have the hosts of "extras", and you will probably have to opt for a digital type if you require an instrument having a comprehensive range of facilities.

Due to their robustness and generally higher specifications, these days I would recommend buying a digital multimeter, particularly if you can find one which offers a wide variety of features at a reasonable price.

Guesstimation

If you are working from test voltages on a circuit diagram it is advisable to scour the "fine print" to see if this specifies the exact nature of the test voltages. They could be theoretical voltages, measurements taken using a digital multimeter, or measurements obtained using a 20k per volt analogue instrument. The voltages specified on many service sheets for commercial equipment are those obtained with a 20k per volt analogue multimeter, but on projects for the amateur they are more likely to be theoretical voltages, or those measured using a digital multimeter.

It is important to know which type of test voltage you are dealing with, because you need to know whether or not to make adjustments to any voltage readings taken from high impedance sections of the circuit. If the "fine print" does not specify the nature of the test voltages, they are almost certainly calculated voltages, or readings taken with a digital multimeter. This is not a certainty though, and the specified voltages have to be treated with a certain amount of discretion.

As pointed out previously, the circuit diagrams for electronic projects do not normally include test voltages, and you must work them out for yourself. Linear circuits almost invariably have bias voltages provided by discrete resistors in potential divider circuits. It is not too difficult to calculate the voltages in a circuit, and in most instances a simple guesstimate should give adequate accuracy. Bear in mind that most circuits are built using five percent tolerance resistors. The tolerance rating of a voltage generated by a potential divider is the same as that of the resistors used in the potential divider. This means that in most cases an error of up to five percent has to be allowed for even before other factors are taken into account.

The accuracy of the multimeter itself is likely to be between about plus and minus one or two percent, but can be poorer than this with cheaper types and (or) when making measurements at well below the full scale value. Do not expect readings to exactly match calculated figures, because "real world" readings on actual circuits will usually be a few percent out. In some cases reading errors of up to about 15 percent can occur without any fault being present in the circuit. Occasionally larger errors can occur, but this normally only happens where there is some built-in loading on the potential divider which you have not taken into account. Finding and allowing for these "hidden" resistances is something we will consider in detail later in this chapter.

Doing Things By Halves

The most simple form of bias circuit is a simple potential divider which has two resistors of equal value. This is the type of bias circuit we have already seen in the circuits of Figure 2.2 and 2.4. There is no need for any calculation with this type of circuit – the bias voltage is equal to half the supply potential. With linear circuits it is standard practice to have the output voltage of each stage at about half the supply voltage. This enables the highest possible signal level to be handled before the amplifier becomes overloaded and the output signal is "clipped" (a very serious form of distortion).

Many circuits, particularly those that are powered from mains power supply units, have a three resistor arrangement of the type shown in Figure 2.5. R1 and C2 act as what is generally termed a "hum trap". This is a lowpass filter which is designed to filter out any mains "hum" or other noise that might otherwise be coupled from the supply lines to the input of an amplifier via the bias circuit. R1 and C2 provide a filtered supply to R2 and R3, with R2 and R3 providing the bias voltage in the normal way.

However, the inclusion of the additional resistor does slightly alter the mathematics of the biasing. In some circuits R2 and R3 are still of equal value, but are much higher in value than R1. This gives very little voltage across R1, so that R2 and R3 can set the centre supply level in the normal way. Obviously there is some voltage drop through R1, but this would typically be no more than about 0.5 volts, which will only marginally drop the output potential from R2 and R3. This does not require any calculations, and it is just a matter of first ensuring that the voltage at the junction of R1 and R2 is slightly less than the supply voltage. A check is then made to ensure that the voltage

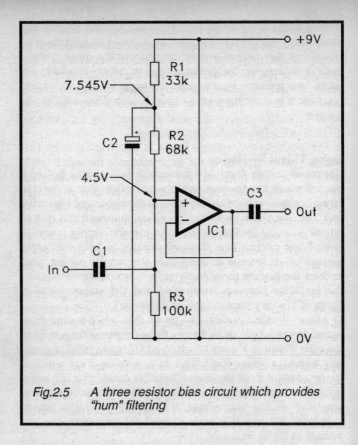

Fig.2.5   A three resistor bias circuit which provides "hum" filtering

at the junction of R2 and R3 is about half the supply voltage, or a little less.

Some circuits have R1 much higher in value relative to the value of R2 and R3. R2 and R3 might still be equal in value, which obviously shifts the bias voltage downwards slightly. This is undesirable, but is not really of any great consequence if the circuit will only handle low level signals. In most circuits the value of R2 is reduced in order to compensate for the higher value of R1, so that the required half supply bias level is still obtained. Either way, the mathematics are slightly more complex than for a simple twin resistor divider circuit.

If the total value of R1 and R2 is roughly the same as the value of R3, the output voltage from the circuit should still be about half the supply voltage. You might simply check this voltage, and if it is correct, investigate the circuit no further. I prefer to make quite sure that everything is in order by checking both voltages. The voltage present across each resistor is equal to its fraction of the total resistance in the potential divider, multiplied by the supply voltage.

For example, the voltage across R3 is calculated by first working out its fraction of the total resistance through R1, R2, and R3. The total resistance is obtained by simply adding the three resistances together, and this gives an answer of 201k (100k + 68k + 33k = 201k). Dividing the value of R1 by 201k gives its share of the total resistance through the network, and this works out at fractionally under 0.50 (100 divided by 201 = 0.4975). Multiplying the supply voltage by 0.5 gives the voltage across R3, which in this case is obviously 4.5 volts (9 volts multiplied by 0.5 = 4.5 volts).

The voltages across R1 and R2 can be calculated in a similar fashion, and dividing their values by 201k provides answers of 0.164 and 0.338. Multiplying these figures by 9 volts gives calculated voltages of 1.476 volts across R1 and 3.042 volts across R2. You can measure the potential across each resistor by connecting the multimeter across each resistor, but the more usual approach is to leave the negative test prod connected to the earth supply (assuming the equipment is of the normal negative earth variety), and then measure all voltages relative to the earth rail. The voltage at the junction of R1 and R2 is equal to the sum of the voltages across R2 and R3, which is 7.545 volts (4.5 volts plus 3.042 volts equals 7.542 volts). Note that the total voltage across the resistors in a potential divider must always equal the applied voltage. This condition is clearly met in this case (the small discrepancy being due to rounding errors).

In these days of electronic calculators there is no difficulty in doing the mathematics associated with voltage calculations, but it is not really worthwhile calculating things to several decimal places when using components that give an error of up to plus and minus 5%. An estimate of the voltage across each resistor is all that is needed. In this example there is no difficulty in estimating the voltages quite accurately. Clearly the total value of R1 and R2 (101k) is about the same as the value of R1, and there is about half the supply voltage at the junction of R2 and R3.

Equally clearly, R1 is about half the value of R2, and it accounts for about one third of the voltage across R1 and R2. This voltage is about half the supply potential, or 4.5 volts in other words. One-third of 4.5 volts is obviously 1.5 volts. R2 has about double the value of R1, and accordingly there is twice as much voltage across this resistor. The voltage across R2 is therefore about three volts. Even with circuits where the mathematics are not quite as straightforward as this, it should still be possible to estimate the approximate fraction of the supply voltage across each resistor in a potential divider.

Unseen Enemy

In most modern circuits any loading of potential dividers by other parts of the circuit is too small to be of significance. With operational amplifiers and integrated circuit audio amplifiers the input resistance of the amplifier is usually many megohms, and insufficient to significantly affect even high value bias circuits. The same is also true of bias circuits which drive any form of field effect transistor (f.e.t.). These have input resistances that are measured in thousands of megohms, or even millions of megohms.

Circuits based on bipolar transistors are a different matter, and they can significantly load the bias network. Where necessary, the circuit designer will take this loading into account, and the output voltage from the amplifier will still be about half the supply voltage, even though the bias circuit appears to provide a substantially higher bias level. The circuit diagram of Figure 2.6 shows a typical high input impedance emitter follower buffer stage, and this illustrates the loading effect of a bipolar stage.

R1 and R2 are the bias resistors, and R3 is the emitter load resistor for TR1. On the face of it, the bias voltage at the junction of R1 and R2 is substantially more than half the supply voltage, because R1 has a value which is much lower than that of R2. In fact it is little less than half that of R2, giving slightly under one third of the supply voltage across R1,

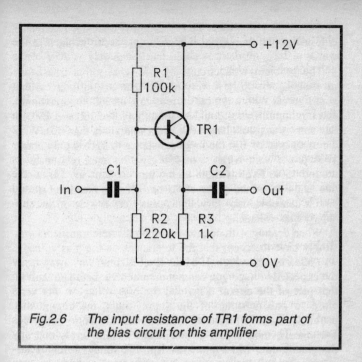

*Fig.2.6   The input resistance of TR1 forms part of
          the bias circuit for this amplifier*

and a little over two thirds of the supply voltage across R2.
With a supply potential of 12 volts there is a little over eight
volts at the junction of R1 and R2.

Matters are rather different when the loading of TR1 is taken
into account. The input resistance of TR1 will be approximately equal to the current gain of TR1 multiplied by the value of
R3. This gives a value which is slightly lower than the actual
input resistance of TR1, but it gives sufficient accuracy for our
purposes. Suppose that the device used for TR1 has a typical
current gain of 200. With R3 at a value of 1k, this gives an input
resistance at the base of TR1 of about 200k or so. This resistance is effectively in parallel with R2, and shunts its value
quite significantly. In fact it gives an effective value of about
105k. This gives fractionally more than half the supply voltage
at the base of TR1. The voltage at TR1's emitter will be the
same, minus about 0.65 volts dropped across the base-emitter

junction. The potential at TR1's emitter is therefore fractionally less than half the supply voltage, or just under 6 volts in other words.

The problem with circuits of this type is that transistors invariably seem to have very high tolerances on their current gain figures. With a typical current gain of 200, the maximum and minimum figures could be something like 100 and 450. In fact some transistors have even wider tolerances than this. With a current gain of 100 the input resistance to TR1 is only about 100k or so, while a figure of 450 gives an input resistance of around 450k. Even without taking into account any variations due to the tolerance rating of R1 and R2, the bias level of the circuit can obviously vary significantly either side of the half supply bias voltage.

When dealing with circuits based on discrete transistors you simply have to accept that the tolerances on the bias voltages will often be quite high. If a bias level is some way away from the expected voltage you can not assume that there is a fault in that part of the circuit. Provided the bias voltage is not very close to one or other of the supply rails, the circuit will probably have sufficient "headroom" to work properly. Fortunately, most faults do not result in bias levels that are marginally out. Most faults result in the voltage levels in the relevant stage being far removed from their correct levels.

Transistor Amplifiers
The emitter follower stage is just one type of transistor amplifier, and there are two others. These are the common emitter and common base types. We will not consider common base amplifiers here as they are something of a rarity. As far as biasing methods are concerned, they are basically the same as common emitter amplifiers anyway. Figure 2.7 shows the circuit diagrams for two versions of the common emitter amplifier.

The configuration shown in Figure 2.7(a) is a very simple one which uses just a single bias resistor, and relies on negative feedback to prevent any large errors in the output bias voltage. The value of R1 is normally made equal to the value of R2 multiplied by the current gain of the transistor. This gives a resistance through the collector and emitter of TR1 that is

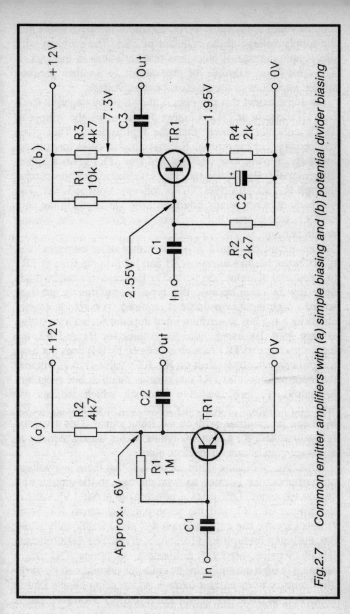

Fig.2.7   Common emitter amplifiers with (a) simple biasing and (b) potential divider biasing

roughly equal to the value of R2, and therefore gives about half the supply voltage at the collector of TR1. The problem with this simple method of biasing is that variations in the gain of TR1 from one example of the circuit to another produce similar variations in the quiescent output voltage.

To some extent this problem is alleviated by negative feedback. If the gain of TR1 is higher than average, the voltage at TR1's collector is lower than the typical level. This gives reduced bias current through R1, and a higher collector voltage. Similarly, a lower than average gain from TR1 gives a higher than normal collector voltage. This gives increased bias current through R1, which drives TR1's collector voltage lower. The feedback does not totally counteract the variations in the gain of TR1, but it does help to keep any errors in the biasing within reason.

The circuit of Figure 2.7(b) is rather more complex, and offers better biasing accuracy. R1 and R2 bias the base of TR1 to a potential of about 2.55 volts. The bias resistors can be made quite low in value because this type of amplifier is not used where a high input impedance is required. A common emitter amplifier has a low to medium input impedance, but a very high voltage gain. By using quite low values for R1 and R2, the input resistance of TR1 (which is boosted by R4) does not have a significant shunting effect on R2. R2's value is 2k7, whereas the input resistance to TR1 could be as much as one megohm. R4 introduces local negative feedback which reduces the amplifier's voltage gain to only about two times at d.c., but C2 bypasses the feedback with an a.c. input signal. This gives the full gain of TR1 for a.c. input signals, which usually equates to a voltage gain of one hundred or more.

This type of biasing relies on the fact that there is a voltage drop of about 0.6 volts or so from the base to the emitter of a silicon transistor. This gives a potential of about 1.95 volts at the emitter of TR1, and the same potential across R4. From Ohm's Law we can calculate that this gives fractionally under one milliamp through R4 (1.95 volts divided by 2000 ohms = 0.000975 amps, or 0.975 milliamps). Assuming TR1 has a reasonably high current gain, its collector current will be virtually identical to its emitter current. Again using Ohm's Law it is possible to work out the voltage across R3. However, this is doing things the hard way. R3 is 2.35 times the value of R4, so the voltage across it will be 2.35 times higher than the voltage across R4. This is clearly about 4.7 volts, and deducting this from the 12 volt supply potential gives 7.3 volts at the collector of TR1.

With potential divider biasing the actual test voltages are usually quite close to the calculated figures. The tolerance of the transistor's current gain may be very high, but the gain of the transistor has little effect on the voltage levels in the circuit. These are largely governed by the ratios of the resistors, and errors should therefore be no more than about 5%, and will often be far less than this. There are no high resistance bias networks in a circuit such as this, and the loading effect of the multimeter will be quite small. In fact the loading of the meter is likely to be so slight as to be of no consequence unless you are using a low sensitivity analogue instrument.

Facts And Figures

Many modern circuits are based on complex integrated circuits which contain numerous stages. So how do you know what test voltages to expect at each pin of a complex linear integrated circuit? In some cases there will still be networks that provide a half supply voltage bias level, and with most audio amplifiers the output voltage should be at about the half supply level even if there is no discrete bias circuit. In the main though, the correct voltage for each pin can only be ascertained by referring to the appropriate data sheet. Some of the larger component retailers sell data sheets for all or most of the integrated circuits that they supply, and the cost is not usually very high. If you run into serious difficulties with a project that uses a complex linear integrated circuit, it is well worthwhile obtaining the relevant data sheet. You are very much "left in the dark" without the requisite data sheet.

Loaded Question

We have already seen that the multimeter can load test points and produce low readings. How do you allow for this loading when making measurements on low current circuits? One approach is to do some calculations and work out the precise effect of meter loading on each test point, but this would be very time consuming, and is not really a very practical proposition. Fortunately, it is not too hard to estimate the loading factor with a fair degree of accuracy. Table 2.1 shows some typical reductions in effective resistance for a digital multimeter having an input resistance of 10 megohms.

Table 2.1

Resistance	Effective Resistance
10M	5M
4M7	3M2
2M2	1M8
1M	909k
470k	448k
220k	215k
100k	99k
47k	46.8k

The loading problem is clearly not a great one when using a digital multimeter (or a high impedance analogue voltmeter). The effective resistance of a 10 megohm resistor is halved, but with a one megohm resistor the reduction is under 10 percent, and with a 100k resistor it is only about one percent. Consequently, it is only when measuring the voltage across a resistor having a value of a few hundred kilohms or more that it is necessary to take the meter loading into account. There is no need for any calculations, since Table 2.1 gives an accurate enough guide to permit a reasonable guesstimate to be made. For example, a resistor having a value of 3M3 would be loaded down to somewhere between 3M2 and 1M8. A reasonable estimate would therefore be about 2M5, which is near enough to the correct figure of 2M481. If you are a perfectionist, you can always work out a full list of loaded resistances for all the E24 series of values from about 10k to 22M.

Loaded Down
Matters are rather less rosy if you use an analogue multimeter, even if it is a 20k per volt type. The meter is likely to be mainly used on the 10 volt range, which gives a load resistance of 200k. This is fifty times lower than the resistance of a digital

multimeter, and loading effects therefore become apparent at relatively low source resistances. Table 2.2 shows the loading effect of a 20k per volt multimeter (set to the 10 volt range) on a wide range of resistors.

Table 2.2

Resistance	Effective Resistance
10M	196k
4M7	192k
2M2	183k
1M	167k
470k	140k
220k	105k
100k	67k
47k	38k
22k	20k
10k	9k5
4k7	4k59
2k2	2k176
1k	995 ohms

When measuring voltages across resistances of one megohm or more it is clear that the loading of the meter is so great that meter readings will be loaded down to a very low level. This is not to say that readings taken from high resistance sources using an analogue multimeter are totally meaningless. If the upper resistor in the potential divider has gone low in value quite a high voltage reading will be obtained, which clearly indicates a fault. Similarly, if there is no deflection of the meter's pointer at all, this indicates that there is a fault. Presumably the upper resistor in the potential divider has gone open circuit, or the lower resistor has gone short circuit.

It can be useful to switch the meter to a higher voltage range, such as the 100 volt range. On this range a 20k per volt multimeter has a resistance of 2 megohms, which gives reduced loading. This should give a higher voltage reading, although the actual deflection of the pointer will still be quite small, and the accuracy of the reading will be quite low. However, if a much higher voltage reading is obtained, it confirms that the low readings are due to meter loading, and not due to a fault which is producing a low voltage at a relatively low source impedance. If the voltage reading remains low, with only very slight deflection of the meter's pointer, there is a fault in that part of the circuit.

For voltages measured across lower resistances of around 470k or less, the voltage measurements become more meaningful, provided you remember to take the loading effect of the meter into account. For resistances below about 22k the loading becomes too small to be of any great significance, and in the main it can simply be ignored.

Start At The Beginning

The general approach taken when making voltage tests is to some extent dictated by your knowledge of the circuit, or lack of it. If you have a list of test voltages, or can confidently estimate the voltage at practically every point in the circuit, then it makes sense to comprehensively work through the circuit from one end to the other. There is a lack of true consensus about the best way of doing this. Some advocate starting at the output and working backwards, some suggest beginning at the input and working forwards, and others recommend starting in the middle and working outwards (which apparently has statistical arguments in its favour).

Any of these methods should find the fault fairly rapidly, but I would suggest the start at the beginning approach. This is not just because it seems more natural and logical to work this way. There is a problem with any method that involves working backwards through the circuit, and this is simply that you are likely to find incorrect voltages that are nothing to do with faults in that part of the circuit. Consider the class B audio power amplifier circuit shown in Figure 2.8. Incidentally, this circuit has been "borrowed" from BP277, "High Power Audio Amplifier Construction", from the same publisher and author as this publication. Refer to BP277 for a detailed description of this circuit.

Suppose that a voltage check at the source terminals of TR4 and TR5 reveals a very low voltage. The obvious assumption would be that the fault was in one of the output transistors. Perhaps TR4 has gone open circuit, or TR5 has gone short

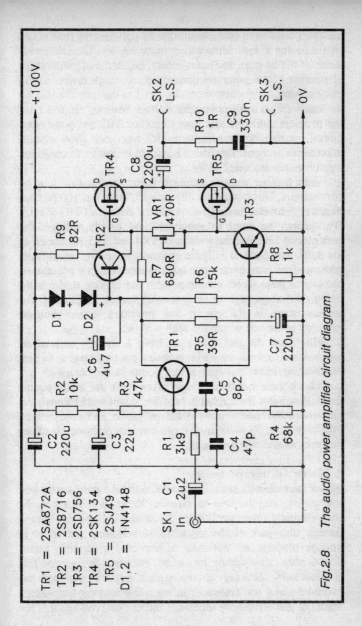

Fig.2.8   The audio power amplifier circuit diagram

TR1 = 2SA872A
TR2 = 2SB716
TR3 = 2SD756
TR4 = 2SK134
TR5 = 2SJ49
D1,2 = 1N4148

57

circuit. This is not a safe assumption though, and the fault could easily be due to a problem earlier in the circuit. The catch with a circuit of this type, and many others, is that the output voltage is governed by a potential divider circuit much earlier in the circuit. A fault anywhere from the input to the output could be the cause of an incorrect output voltage reading. In this case the problem could be that load transistor TR2 has gone open circuit, or that driver transistor TR3 has gone short circuit. Alternatively, input transistor TR1 could be faulty, as could the input bias resistors (R2 to R4).

When making voltage checks it is essential not to jump to conclusions. This circuit has three stages, but it has 100 percent negative feedback from the output to the emitter of TR1 via R7. By biasing the input to about half the supply voltage, the collector of TR3 and the sources of TR4 and TR5 are biased to the same potential. It is quite common for power amplifiers, preamplifiers, and even some quite complex signal processing circuits to have direct coupling, with the biasing at the input being carried through to several other stages. In general, the earliest stage in the circuit that provides suspect voltage readings is the one where the fault will lie.

With some circuits you may have a limited amount of information to work on, and it is then a matter of trying to find or calculate likely voltages at any points in the circuit so you can check them against readings taken from the faulty equipment. If possible it is probably best if you still work through the circuit in a methodical manner, but with these awkward circuits you may have to work in a more random fashion, checking voltages as and when you can.

A Matter Of Interpretation
As we have already seen, it is essential to take great care when interpreting results. Due to various factors, readings may be well removed from specified or calculated voltage levels even though that part of the circuit is functioning perfectly. If voltage readings are not quite as expected it certainly raises doubts about that part of the circuit, but you can find yourself continuously "barking up the wrong tree" if you get too pedantic about test results. You are really looking for voltage readings that are clearly incorrect, rather than readings that are

marginally out.

The main problem in interpreting results is that a clearly incorrect voltage reading will not usually indicate exactly which component is at fault. It is a common mistake for beginners to read too much into the results of voltage checks, leading to them jump to conclusions. Voltage checks will usually let you home-in on the stage where the fault lies, but further checks will then be needed in order to locate the precise cause of the problem.

If we consider the circuit of Figure 2.8 again, let us assume that the voltage at the base of TR1 is very low, or perhaps even zero. This would tend to suggest that there is a fault in the bias circuit (R2 to R4). R4 could have gone short circuit (i.e. it's providing a short-circuit). The fault is just as likely to be due to R2 or R3 having gone open circuit (i.e. having an extremely high resistance). With a two resistor potential divider, the only way of finding out is to measure the resistance of both components.

In this case there are three resistors in the network, and measuring the voltage at the junction of R2 and R3 should give some useful information. If the voltage here is very low, it is likely that the problem is due to R2 having gone open circuit. A high test voltage would suggest that R2 is all right, and that it is still permitting an appreciable current flow. A fault in R3 or R4 would then be a more likely cause of the problem.

On the face of it, there is no problem if the values of resistors are measured in-circuit. In practice this method does not work very well because there are various resistances in parallel with the resistor you are checking. These resistances are usually connected across the test resistor in a round-about manner, but they are still there, and can significantly affect results. Diode junctions in transistors, integrated circuits, etc., are a major cause of problems, and using a resistance meter that operates with a very low test voltage is helpful by effectively eliminating them. If the test voltage never exceeds about 0.5 volts, the silicon diode junctions can not become forward biased, and can not significantly affect readings.

The problem of parallel resistance can not be totally avoided using a low voltage resistance meter, since there are true resistances in the circuit that will still be there, however low the test voltage. Nevertheless, in-circuit resistance readings can be useful if you bear in mind that parallel resistances can only reduce the effective value of a resistor, they can not increase it. If a resistance reading is lower than the marked value of the resistor, this does not necessarily indicate that the resistor is faulty. The low reading could be due to shunting of the resistor by other resistances in the circuit. On the other hand, if the resistance reading is higher than the marked value, the resistor must be faulty.

In order to reliably measure the value of a resistor, one of the leadout wires should be desoldered from the circuit board so that the influence of other resistances in the circuit is totally removed. Disconnecting one leadout wire is not difficult, but take care not to damage the copper track and pad when reconnecting it. Ideally you should use proper desoldering equipment to remove the solder from the original joint. There should then be no difficulty in pulling the lead away from the board, making the measurement, pushing the lead back into place, and soldering it in place once again.

You can simply apply the hot bit to the iron and pull the lead free. After making the measurement the iron can be applied to the joint once again and the lead can be pushed back in place. However, this invites problems with damage to the copper track and pad, or with "dry" joints. Working on circuits with the power applied is another good way of adding faults rather than repairing them! Always switch off the project before doing any soldering or desoldering. In the case of a mains powered project, also disconnect it from the mains outlet.

Jumping To Conclusions

When dealing with voltage measurements it is easy to get embroiled with resistor values and potential dividers, overlooking the fact that incorrect voltages can be produced by other components. A capacitor normally exhibits a very high resistance after its initial charge current has been taken up. A capacitor should therefore have no significant affect on the voltages in a circuit. However, a faulty capacitor can, and often does, place a virtual short-circuit across its leads. With a non-electrolytic capacitor this normally occurs because of physical damage which produces a hole in the dielectric. This enables the two metal plates to touch, producing the short-circuit. Problems are more common with electrolytic capacitors, and the main cause of faults seems to be a general breakdown of the dielectric, producing a very low resistance rather than a true short circuit across the two metal plates.

In either case there will almost certainly be some affect on the d.c. levels in the circuit. Returning to the circuit of Figure 2.8 and our example fault which is producing an extremely low input bias voltage. This could be caused by a fault in C3. A low resistance through C3 would pull the junction of R2 and R3 to a very low voltage, taking the base of TR1 to a low voltage as well. If C3 was the cause of the fault, disconnecting one of its leads should restore the d.c. levels in the circuit, but might result in a lot of "hum" and other noise on the output of the amplifier, and could even cause instability. However, if effectively removing C3 from the circuit causes it to burst into some form of life, replacing C3 should cure the fault.

A fault in C4 could also "pull" the base of TR1 down to a low voltage. Faults in capacitors as low as 47p in value are quite rare, and when they do occur they are generally of the open circuit and not the short circuit variety. A small capacitor producing a short-circuit can not be ruled out, but I would be inclined to investigate other possibilities first.

I have occasionally encountered amplifiers which seem to work all right with no input lead attached, with the usual background "hiss" being produced from the speaker. With an input connected to the amplifier, an initial "thud" is followed by silence. The usual cause of the problem is that the input coupling capacitor (C1 in this case) is faulty, or, more usually, is an electrolytic type connected the wrong way round. With any fault that only occurs under certain conditions it pays to look carefully at what changes in the circuit when the fault condition occurs. A more obvious example would be where a piece of test equipment functions on every range but one. The problem could be a faulty range switch, but it is more likely that one of the components switched in on the faulty range is either broken or simply not connected properly.

Semiconductors

I suppose that it is fair to say that semiconductors are one of the more frequent causes of faults. This is probably not due to them being any less reliable than other components, but is due to them being more vulnerable to damage. In particular, they are easily damaged if you spend rather too long soldering them into circuit. Even though they are a likely cause of problems, I tend to check other possibilities first. This is simply because it is generally easier to check resistors and capacitors than it is to make meaningful voltage checks on transistors and integrated circuits.

In our example circuit of Figure 2.8 the base of TR1 should be biased to a little over half the supply voltage. Its emitter terminal should be about 0.65 volts higher in voltage. Note that TR1 is a p.n.p. transistor, and that the base is therefore negative of the emitter. TR1's collector directly drives the base of TR3, and the base of TR3 should be at about 0.65 volts. A very low voltage at the base of TR1 could be caused by TR1 going short circuit between its base and collector terminals. Transistors do sometimes go wrong in a minor way, such as having a slightly higher than normal leakage level, but it seems to be more normal for a complete breakdown. This is usually in the form of a total lack of connections between the terminals, the terminals short-circuited together, or a combination of the two.

If the problem was due to a short circuit across the base and collector terminals of TR1, this would be indicated by the base and collector voltages both being identical, or very nearly so, at about 0.65 volts. Testing the leadouts of a transistor to see if any are at the same voltage is a useful general test. Damaged transistors often seem to exhibit this characteristic. It is also useful to remember that a silicon transistor when biased into conduction will have a voltage difference of about 0.65 volts across its base and emitter terminals. If two terminals are at the same potential, or this 0.65 voltage difference is absent, it is likely that the device is faulty.

If you suspect that a transistor is faulty, the only sure way to find out is to totally remove it from the circuit board and test it. Methods of testing components, including transistors, are discussed in Chapter 4.

One Way

Diodes are very simple semiconductors, but are as vulnerable to heat damage as other semiconductors. Some types also seem to be physically quite weak, and relatively easily damaged. In the circuit of Figure 2.8 there are two diodes which are used as part of a constant current generator based on TR2. This acts as the collector load for driver transistor TR3. The two diodes are forward biased by R6, and effectively used as low voltage zener diodes. The voltage across each diode should be about 0.65 volts, giving approximately 1.3 volts less than the supply voltage at the base of TR2. This can easily be checked with a multimeter, but an error here could obviously be caused by problems with other components.

Suppose that the base of TR2 is only 0.65 volts below the positive supply potential. One possibility is that either D1 or D2 has gone short circuit, effectively leaving just one diode in the circuit. On the other hand, the problem could be due to R9 having gone short circuit. The base-emitter junction of TR1 will then limit the voltage drop to only about 0.65 volts, effectively cutting D1 and D2 out of the circuit. With most voltage checks that indicate a problem, there is more than one possible cause of the problem, and further investigation will be needed in order to get things properly sorted out.

Virtually all multimeters can be used to check diodes, as can most continuity testers (see Chapter 4). The basic action of a diode is to allow a current to flow in one direction, but to block a flow of current in the opposite direction. In terms of conventional current flow, a diode permits a flow of current from the anode to the cathode. Testing diodes in-circuit is not a totally reliable way of doing things because there can be resistances and other diode junctions in parallel with the test component. This can make it appear as though a diode is conducting when it is not. A diode that is not conducting in the forward direction can appear to be functioning correctly, and one that does not conduct in the reverse direction may appear to do so.

If an in-circuit diode seems to conduct in the forward direction, and has a high resistance in the opposite direction, then it is probably all right. However, the only sure way of finding out is to disconnect one lead and retest the diode. If a diode appears to conduct in both directions, then it is likely that the diode is faulty. Once again though, it is necessary to disconnect one lead and retest the component in order to be sure that it is not functioning. An in-circuit diode is certainly faulty if it fails to conduct in either direction.

Hidden Faults

You may occasionally be faced with an intriguing project where all the voltages seem quite plausible, but the unit fails to work. This can sometimes be due to the resistance of the meter effectively replacing a broken resistor in the circuit. Using our example circuit of Figure 2.8 once again, suppose that R6 is faulty, and is providing a very high resistance.

On the face of it, measuring the voltage at the base of TR2 should provide an erroneous reading, but would it actually do so? With R6 effectively removed from the circuit, the multimeter is reading the supply voltage via D1 and D2, and it will read the 100 volt supply potential minus the 1.3 volts or thereabouts dropped through the two diodes. In other words, it provides much the same reading with or without R6 in circuit. The resistance of the multimeter provides the forward bias to the diodes, and gives the appearance of normality.

This type of fault can be difficult to find, and if all the circuit voltages seem correct it can be worthwhile rechecking them, but referenced to the other supply rail. This diode circuit is providing a voltage that is stabilised at around 1.3 volts below the positive supply potential, so it would really be more logical to measure the 1.3 volts across D1 and D2, rather than the 98.7 volts across R6. Apart from other considerations, a small error in a potential of around 100 volts will be far more difficult to detect than a large error in a potential of about 1.3 volts. Also, if R6 is open circuit, there will be no current feed into D1 and D2 with this method of measurement, and therefore no voltage across these two diodes. This would clearly indicate a fault in this part of the circuit, with either D1 and D2 both having gone short circuit, or (more probably) R6 having gone open circuit.

With the original method of checking this voltage it is possible that on connecting the multimeter to the circuit it would to some extent burst into life. This would be more likely when using an analogue multimeter, with its lower resistance. The lower resistance would give a stronger bias to the base of TR2, which would be more likely to bring the circuit into a partially functioning state. If adding the multimeter to part of a circuit alleviates the fault to some degree, it is clearly worth taking a closer look at this part of the circuit. It does not always indicate that the fault is in that area of the circuit, but in most cases the faulty component will not be too far away.

Incapacitated

It tends to be assumed that a fault will always produce tell-tale voltage errors in some part of the circuit, but this is not really the case. Faults in semiconductors, resistors, and inductors will normally produce at least one incorrect voltage, but can not be relied upon to do so. Capacitors are a different matter though. As we have already seen, a capacitor that has gone short circuit will almost certainly produce incorrect voltage levels. The same is not true of a capacitor that has gone open circuit. Whether working correctly or open circuit, its resistance will be very high, and it will have no influence on the circuit voltages.

Sometimes the nature of the fault will strongly suggest that a capacitor is at fault. Returning once again to the circuit of Figure 2.8, the purpose of C3 is to provide some "hum" and general noise filtering in the bias circuit. If the amplifier seems to have rather a high background "hum" level, and the current drain of the circuit is not excessive, then the obvious starting point is to investigate filter capacitors such as C3. Faulty filtering and decoupling capacitors can also give problems with low frequency instability, which will often be in the form of the amplifier oscillating at a frequency of a few hertz. This is sometimes called "motor-boating", as it tends to produce a sound which is reminiscent of an old fashioned motorboat. If this form of instability should occur, the obvious starting point is to investigate the filter and decoupling capacitors (C2, C3, and C6 in this example), rather than making voltage tests.

If an amplifier exhibits very low gain, but in other respects seems to be working, this suggests that the capacitor in a negative feedback network is open circuit. In the circuit of Figure 2.8 there is only one capacitor of this type, and this is C7. The circuit has 100 percent negative feedback at d.c., which makes it easy to provide accurate biasing. Simply bias the input to about half the supply voltage, and the output will also be biased to the same level. Some of the feedback must be removed at audio frequencies in order to give the circuit a useful amount of voltage gain, and this is the purpose of C7 and R5. C7 decouples the negative feedback, and R5 limits the amount of feedback that is removed. It is normal to leave a substantial amount of feedback, as this improves the amplifier's distortion performance.

The voltage gain of the circuit is approximately equal to the value of R7 divided by the value of R5. If C7 goes open circuit, all the feedback is left intact, and the circuit only has unity voltage gain at audio frequencies. R5 going high in value or R7 going low in value could have much the same effect, so some component testing would be needed in order to determine which component was faulty. Note that faults in R5 and R7 might not produce any incorrect voltages in the circuit, but would prevent it from functioning correctly. Faulty resistors producing changed voltage readings is quite definitely not a certainty, and voltage tests will not always reveal faults.

In The Main
An important point that must be made here is that it is dangerous to test mains powered circuits while they are connected to the mains power supply. It is obviously impossible to make voltage checks unless the equipment is plugged into the mains supply and switched on. Great care must therefore be taken when making voltage checks on mains powered equipment, or any other checks that require the equipment to be switched on. Electronic workshops should really have power sockets fed from the mains supply via an isolation transformer. In other words, they should be fed from the mains supply via a transformer which has 230 volt primary and secondary windings. The 230 volt output from the transformer is still very dangerous, but the risk of a dangerous shock to earth is greatly reduced. Obviously few amateur electronics enthusiasts have a workshop which is powered by way of an isolation transformer.

Most mains powered electronic projects include a mains isolation transformer which has a low voltage output, and one of the supply rails of the equipment is usually earthed. This gives little risk of a severe electric shock from most of the circuit, provided a serious mistake has not been made during the construction of the unit. **It is essential to thoroughly check the power supply of a mains powered project before switching the unit on, and the temptation to give just a cursory check here should be overcome.** Remember that it is not just the project that could be harmed if there is a mistake in the power supply wiring. The mains supply is potentially lethal, and has to be treated as such. **Beginners at electronic project construction should not build mains powered projects, and should certainly not undertake fault finding on a mains powered project while it is connected to the mains supply.**

Experienced constructors must rigidly observe the standard safety precautions when undertaking fault finding on mains powered projects. Obviously you must make quite sure that you do not come into contact with any exposed mains wiring. Ideally, all exposed mains wiring, such as the connections to the on/off switch, should be insulated at the construction stage. It will of course be necessary to remove this insulation if testing of the mains wiring becomes necessary. Make certain that the unit is unplugged from the mains supply before removing the insulation. Simply switching off at the mains outlet or at the on/off switch of the equipment is not sufficient, and would probably result in a severe electric shock being sustained.

In fact most testing of the input section of the power supply can be undertaken with the project unplugged from the mains supply. It clearly makes sense to, as far as possible, make safe tests with the project unplugged from the mains, rather than making potentially dangerous tests with the unit connected to the mains. With the unit unplugged from the mains supply, testing is largely a matter of making continuity checks to ensure that the on/off switch is functioning, the fuse is not blown, and the mains lead connects through to the mains plug reliably. If possible, avoid making any voltage checks on parts of the circuit that connect to the mains supply, and take due care if you do make any such tests.

When dealing with mains powered projects it is a good idea to use the old ploy of keeping one hand in your pocket while testing the equipment. This may seem like rather odd advice, but the point of doing this is that you can not end up with one hand touching a "live" wire and the other connected to earth. This avoids the risk of a severe shock to earth, from one hand to the other via vital organs, including the heart. You can still get a major jolt, but the risk of receiving a lethal electric shock is greatly diminished.

Apart from making sure that you do not accidentally touch any exposed mains wiring, also make certain that you do not accidentally bridge any points in the circuit with the test prods. Even if you survive intact, it is likely that every semiconductor in the circuit would be destroyed. Clip type test prods are rather safer for this kind of testing than the type which has long metal prods.

If you have a suitable bench power supply unit, it is possible to power the unit under test from this rather than the mains supply. This enables voltage checks to be made on the faulty unit without it being directly connected to the mains supply. Simply disconnect the secondary of the unit's mains transformer from the circuit board, and connect the bench power supply in its place. Remember to set the bench power supply for a suitable output voltage before switching it on.

If the unit under test does not have a stabilised supply, the bench supply should be set for about one volt more than the required supply voltage. The extra voltage is needed in order to allow for the voltage drop through the rectifiers. If the unit under test includes a series voltage regulator in its supply circuit, the output potential from the bench supply must be set about four volts higher than the required supply voltage. This allows for the voltage drops through the rectifiers and the voltage regulator.

Short Supply

Figure 2.9 shows the circuit diagram for a typical stabilised mains power supply. This uses push-pull full-wave rectification with regulation provided by IC1. The latter is a 78** series 15 volt monolithic voltage regulator. Smoothing is provided by C1. The purpose of C2 and C3 is to provide high frequency supply decoupling for IC1, and this helps to prevent it from becoming unstable.

We will assume here that the mains supply is getting through to step-down and isolation transformer T1, and that it is supplying an appropriate a.c. voltage to the rectifier circuit. We will also assume that a check has been made to ensure that the

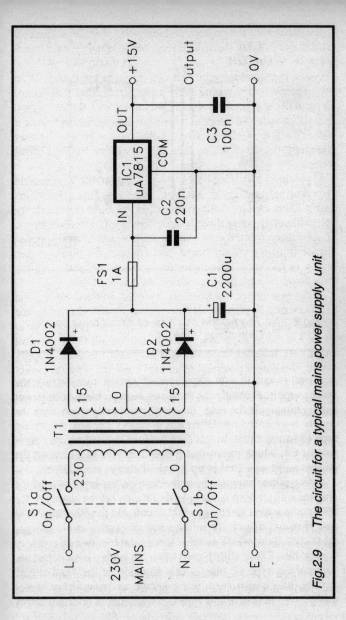

Fig.2.9   The circuit for a typical mains power supply unit

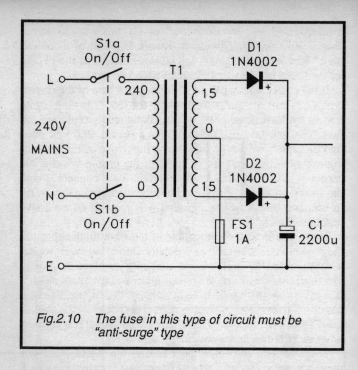

Fig.2.10   *The fuse in this type of circuit must be "anti-surge" type*

problem is not due to the supplied circuit overloading the power supply. Probably the most common problem with power supply circuits is the fuse "blowing" practically every time the supply is switched on. Often this is simply because the wrong type of fuse is fitted. In this case the fuse is fitted on the output side of C1, which means that it does not have to withstand the current surge as C1 takes up its initial charge at switch-on.

Some power supplies have the fuse on the input side of C1 (Figure 2.10), which is better in that it cuts off the supply to C1 if this component should go short circuit. On the other hand, the fuse then has to pass the initial surge of current as C1 charges up at switch-on, which more or less guarantees that an ordinary "quick-blow" fuse will "blow" when the supply is switched on. The correct type of fuse in this situation is the "anti-surge" variety, which also seem to be known as "time-delay" fuses these days. A fuse of this type can withstand a brief but heavy overload, and should not "blow" as C1 takes up its initial charge. An "anti-surge" fuse will work in place of a "quick-blow" type incidentally, but will be less efficient as it will take longer to cut off the supply if an overload occurs.

If the power supply circuit is fitted with a fuse of the correct type, and there are still problems with the fuse "blowing" quite frequently, there is no point in just continuously replacing the fuse. The fuse will be "blowing" for a reason, and you must find that reason. With the fuse on the input side of the smoothing capacitor, the most likely cause of the problem is that the capacitor has a very high leakage current (or is connected with the wrong polarity!). The capacitor might get noticeably warm in use, and this is a sure sign that it is passing an excessive leakage current.

If the fuse is on the output side of the smoothing capacitor, the problem might be that the regulator chip is faulty. However, a faulty regulator will almost certainly produce a grossly incorrect output voltage. With the output voltage about right, it is more likely that the fault is actually in the supplied circuit, causing it to draw an excessive current and "blow" the fuse. A quick check on the output current of the supply will show whether or not an excessive current is flowing.

There should, of course, be a fuse in the mains plug. The mains current consumption of most projects is extremely small, and a fault on the output side of the mains transformer is unlikely to "blow" the mains fuse. In the event that the fuse in the plug "blows", it is likely that the problem is due to a faulty mains transformer or on/off switch. Alternatively, there could be a problem with the mains lead or the connections to the plug.

Some projects include a built-in fuse in the mains wiring. When building projects of this type always use a proper panel mounting fuse-holder that is intended for this type of thing. Panel mounting holders are designed to permit the fuse to be changed safely even if the unit should be inadvertently left connected to the mains supply. With chassis mounting fuses you inevitably come into contact with the fuse terminals when fitting or removing the fuse. This would almost certainly result in a severe electric shock if the fuse was in "live" wiring.

Peak Performance

Most power supply circuits are very simple, and it should not take long to discover any faults. The uninitiated usually find voltage across the smoothing capacitor is higher than expected. You have to bear in mind here that (say) 18 volts a.c. does not produce 18 volts d.c. when rectified and smoothed. The capacitor charges up to the peak a.c. voltage, which is 1.414 times greater than the r.m.s. output voltage from the transformer. For an 18 volt transformer this gives 25.452 volts across the smoothing capacitor. The voltage drop through the rectifiers has to be taken into account though, and this reduces the d.c. output voltage by around 0.6 to 1.2 volts (1.2 to 2.4 volts for a bridge rectifier).

In theory this gives about 21.5 volts across C1. In practice the output voltage is to a large extent dependent on the current drain from the power supply. When lightly loaded it is likely that the voltage across the smoothing capacitor will actually be about 1.5 times the rated output voltage of the transformer. Under heavy loading this voltage will fall substantially, but it will still be more than the a.c. voltage rating of T1. The voltage across C1 should therefore be somewhere in the range 19 to 25 volts. If the polarity of the voltage is wrong, the rectifiers are connected the wrong way round! If there is no voltage across C1, either one rectifier is connected with the wrong polarity, or both the rectifiers are faulty.

In general, the input potential to a voltage regulator is at least 3 volts more than its output voltage rating. With a smaller voltage difference there will be a lot of ripple on the output, and the output voltage might drop below the voltage rating of the regulator. If the voltage across C1 is about right, but the output voltage from IC1 is not, then it is virtually certain that IC1 is faulty. C2 or C3 could have gone short circuit, but it is virtually certain that the faulty component would "blow" if this were to happen. The rising smoke would then give a good clue as to the nature of the fault!

Some mains powered circuits, such as mains power controllers, do not include a mains transformer. Testing circuits of this type with the power applied has to be regarded as a risky business, and I would strongly advise against it. It is much better to make safe tests with the unit disconnected from the mains supply. Circuits of this type are mostly relatively simple, and faults can usually be traced using continuity checks, component substitution, etc.

Whose Fault

In this discussion of voltage testing I have tended to talk in terms of components going short circuit or open circuit. It is only fair to point out that in my experience it is very rare for components to become faulty. The resistor that appears to be open circuit often proves to be functioning perfectly once it has been removed from the circuit. The real problem was a "dry" joint or a damaged printed circuit track, and not a faulty resistor. Similarly, transistors which seem to have gone short circuit often perform perfectly when removed from the circuit and tested. Again, the true nature of the problem usually turns out to be something like a solder bridge on the circuit board.

It is important to back-up voltage tests with components tests, continuity checks, etc., to ensure that the apparent fault is the real one. Otherwise you may end up throwing away perfectly good components, or repairing faults only to find that they still persist. Fault finding on your projects will be easier if you are prepared to admit to occasional mistakes.

Ins And Outs

Voltage tests are not the only approach to fault finding on linear equipment. The alternative is to feed an input signal into the faulty equipment, and then test for the signal at various points in the circuit. This method is obviously not applicable with all types of circuit, and would be of no use with power supplies, signal generators, model train controllers, and the like. It is applicable to most audio and radio equipment though, including musical effects units and other signal processing equipment.

In order to use this system it is necessary to have equipment that can provide a suitable test signal, and further equipment to test for the signal at various points in the circuit. In most cases it is not necessary to have some form of signal generator, as the normal signal source (guitar, CD player, or whatever) can be used to provide the test signal. Some form of signal tracer is essential though. This can be as simple as a crystal earphone

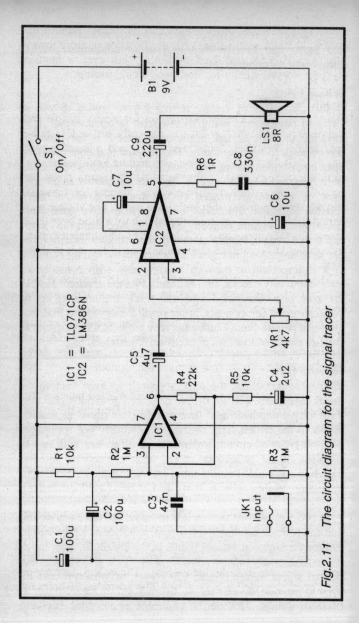

Fig.2.11   The circuit diagram for the signal tracer

plus some test leads, or as complex as the latest "state of the art" multi-beam oscilloscope. An oscilloscope is more than a little desirable for this kind of testing, but even a humble crystal earphone will suffice for much signal tracing.

Signal Tracer

Figure 2.11 shows the circuit diagram for a very simple and inexpensive signal tracer. This is basically just a low noise operational amplifier input stage (IC1), and a small power amplifier (IC2). The output drives a miniature loudspeaker, and output powers of up to a few hundred milliwatts r.m.s. are possible. This gives more than adequate volume for a general purpose test-bench amplifier and signal tracer. The voltage gain provided by IC1 is quite modest, and is only a little over three times. The main function of IC1 is to act as a high input impedance buffer stage, and the input impedance of the unit is about 500k.

Most of the voltage gain is provided by IC2. The closed loop voltage gain of IC2 is controlled by a capacitor and a resistor connected between pins one and eight. In this case we are effectively using a resistance of zero, which results in IC2 operating at its highest possible closed loop gain. This gives excellent sensitivity, which enables the unit to detect very low level signals, such as the output from a microphone or very low output guitar pick-up.

VR1 is the volume control, and it is connected between the preamplifier and power amplifier stages. Bear in mind that strong input signals of more than about two volts peak-to-peak will overload IC1, which is ahead of the volume control. If for some reason it is deemed necessary to use the unit with very high level input signals, the input signal should be coupled to the unit via an attenuator probe. This can simply consist of a set of test leads having a resistor of around 4M7 in series with the non-earth test prod. Due to the high sensitivity of the amplifier it is essential to use screened test leads (as used with oscilloscopes, etc.).

Figure 2.12 shows a suitable stripboard layout for this project, together with the hard wiring. The underside view of the board is provided in Figure 2.13. The board has 39 holes by 18 copper strips. Construction of the unit is fairly straight-

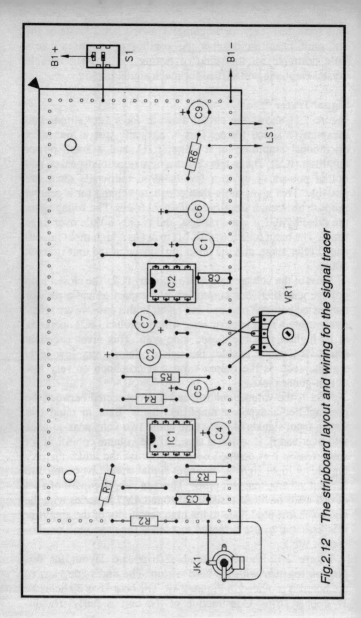

Fig.2.12   The stripboard layout and wiring for the signal tracer

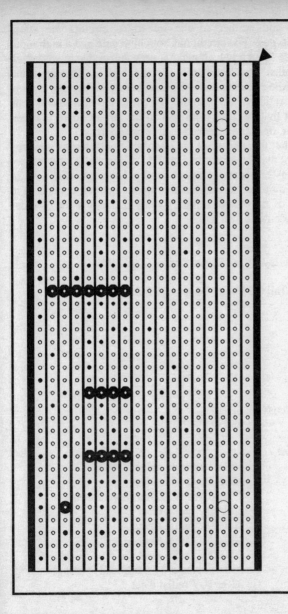

Fig.2.13   The underside of the signal tracer board

forward, and neither of the integrated circuits are static sensitive types. The circuit has both high gain and a high input impedance though, which make it very vulnerable to stray pick up of mains "hum" and other electrical noise. The input and output of the circuit are out-of-phase, but instability due to stray feedback remains a possibility. To avoid these problems it is important that the lead from JK1 to the circuit board is either very short, or that a screened lead is used here.

Note that this unit must only be used to test mains powered equipment that has an earthed chassis, and includes a mains isolation transformer in its power supply. It must not be used to test any equipment which has the supplied circuit connected to one side of the mains supply (which includes a lot of older ready-made radio sets, etc.).

Components List for Signal Tracer (Fig. 2.11)

Resistors (all 0.25 watt 5% carbon film)

R1	10k
R2	1M
R3	1M
R4	22k
R5	10k
R6	1R

Potentiometer

VR1	4k7 log carbon

Capacitors

C1	100μ 10V radial elect
C2	100μ 10V radial elect
C3	47n polyester (7.5mm lead spacing)
C4	2μ2 50V radial elect
C5	4μ7 50V radial elect
C6	10μ 25V radial elect
C7	10μ 25V radial elect
C8	330n polyester (7.5mm lead spacing)
C9	220μ 10V radial elect

Semiconductors

| IC1 | TL071CP or similar |
| IC2 | LM386N or LM386N-1 |

Miscellaneous

S1	SPST min toggle switch
B1	9 volt (PP3 size)
LS1	Miniature 8 ohm impedance loudspeaker
JK1	3.5mm jack socket

Medium size instrument case, 0.1 inch matrix stripboard panel having 39 by 18 holes, control knob, test leads with plug, battery connector, wire, solder, etc.

In Use

As an example of how the signal tracer can be used, assume that the four channel audio mixer circuit of Figure 2.14 is failing to produce an output with a microphone connected to SK1, but is working fine when used with the three high level inputs (SK2 to SK4). This circuit has been "borrowed" from BP363, "Practical Electronic Music Projects", from the same publisher and author as this publication.

It would seem to be reasonable to assume that the summing mode mixer stage based on IC3 is working properly, and that the fault is in the microphone preamplifier based on IC1 and IC2. The first thing to do is to provide the preamplifier with an input signal. This could be a low level sinewave signal from a signal generator, but a microphone with sound provided by a radio set will work just as well for this type of testing. In fact there is something to be said for having things as normal as possible when fault finding, and in this respect the microphone is better than using a signal generator.

The first test is to ensure that a signal is being received at SK1. The problem could be due to a faulty microphone lead, a fault in SK1, or an accidental short circuit on SK1 due to some excess solder on one of the joints. If the signal is getting through to SK1 correctly, the next test is made at the positive terminal of C2. This checks whether or not the signal is getting through C2 correctly. Even if C2 is seriously faulty, it is possible that a certain amount of signal will make it through to the positive terminal. A faulty capacitor will often provide a

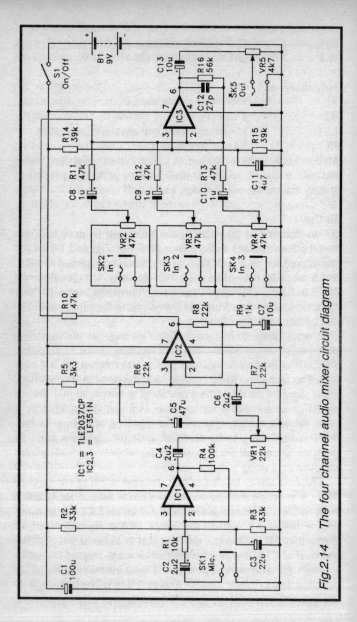

Fig.2.14   The four channel audio mixer circuit diagram

very low capacitance that will provide a small amount of coupling. However, the detected signal will be relatively weak and will have a strong treble content with little or no bass signal.

There is not much point in checking for the signal at the inputs of an operational amplifier used in the inverting mode. The non-inverting input (pin 3) is biased to half the supply voltage, and does not receive the input signal. What is termed a "virtual earth" is formed at the inverting input (pin 2), and no signal should be detectable here either. On the other hand, you can use a signal tracer to check that no signal is present in places where there should be no signal. If checks on the inputs of IC1 show the signal to be present, then there is a problem in this part of the circuit.

If these tests provide normal results, subsequent tests are made at various points along the signal path. R1 and R4 set the voltage gain of IC1 at about ten times, so the signal at the output of IC1 (pin 6) should be substantially stronger than the input signal. The strength of the signal at the wiper of VR1 depends on the setting of this control. It should be possible to vary the signal level from zero with VR1 fully backed-off, to the full output level from IC1 with VR1 fully advanced. IC2 is a non-inverting mode circuit, and the next check is to ensure that the signal is getting through C6 and reaching IC2's non-inverting input. A virtual earth is still produced at the inverting input in this mode, and consequently there should be no significant signal present at pin 2 of IC2.

If the output level from the microphone preamplifier is very low rather than totally absent, the problem could be due to a fault in C7. Testing for a signal at the positive terminal of this capacitor will show whether or not it is functioning correctly. If a strong signal is detected (about the same level as the input to IC2), C7 is obviously not functioning correctly. If no signal is detected, it is virtually certain that C7 is working all right. R8 and R9 set the closed-loop voltage gain of IC2 at about 23 times, so quite a strong output signal should be produced at pin six of IC2 if the two amplifier stages are functioning correctly.

With the other three inputs functioning normally, it is unlikely that a properly amplified output signal will be obtained from IC2, with none of this signal then making it through to the

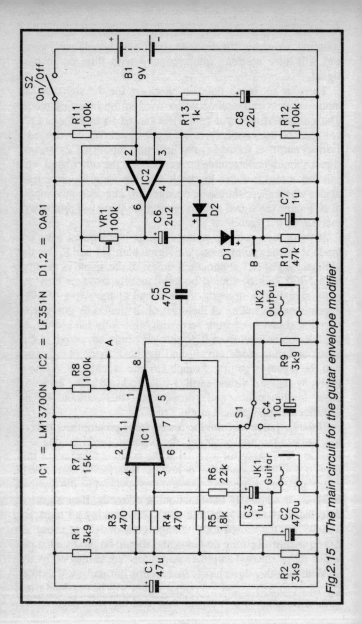

Fig.2.15 The main circuit for the guitar envelope modifier

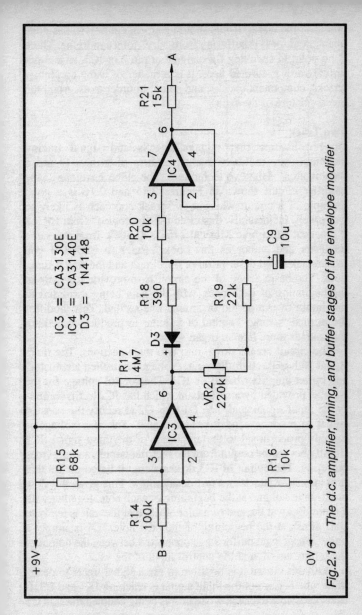

Fig.2.16   The d.c. amplifier, timing, and buffer stages of the envelope modifier

IC3 = CA3130E
IC4 = CA3140E
D3 = 1N4148

83

output of the mixer. If this should happen, either R10 has gone open circuit or it is suffering from "dry" joint syndrome. There is no point in checking for a signal at pin 2 of IC3, as another virtual earth is formed here. It is a matter of using continuity checks, component checks, and so on, in order to ascertain the precise nature of the fault.

Two Track

Do not assume that voltage checks and signal tracing techniques are mutually exclusive. It is often best to use a combination of the two techniques. The guitar envelope shape modifier circuit shown in Figures 2.15 and 2.16 is a good example of a circuit where a two track approach is likely to work well. Incidentally, this circuit is "borrowed" from BP368 ("Practical Electronic Musical Effects Units"), from the same publisher and author as this book. Refer to BP368 if you require a detailed description of the circuit and the way it functions. The basic action of the circuit is to provide low gain at the beginning of each note, with the gain being increased to maximum over a period of around one second. This modifies the normal "twangy" sound of a guitar to produce something that sounds more like an organ sound.

The circuit breaks down into two main sections. The main signal path is through the v.c.a. (voltage controlled attenuator) and buffer amplifier based on IC1. The control voltage for the v.c.a. is provided by a side-chain which has IC2 to first amplify the input signal, and then D1 plus D2 to rectify the boosted signal to produce a positive d.c. signal. This d.c. voltage is roughly proportional to the amplitude of the input signal. IC3 slightly boosts the output from the rectifier circuit, and provides buffering. The output of IC3 drives a circuit based on D3 that provides slow attack and fast decay times. This gives the slow build-up in volume at the beginning of each note, together with a rapid decay at the end of each note so that the unit is ready to start afresh at the beginning of the next note. IC4 is simply a unity voltage gain buffer stage connected between the output of the timing circuit and the control input of the v.c.a.

With this circuit it is possible to use a signal tracer to determine whether or not the input signal is reaching JK1 and C3. It is also possible to check whether it is being coupled through C5 to the non-inverting input of IC2, with an amplified version of the signal appearing at the output of IC2. It is not possible to check much further using a signal tracer though. The signal should be coupled through C6 to the twin diode rectifier, but thereafter the circuit is dealing with varying d.c. levels, and not a.c. signals. This renders a signal tracer of little further use. A check could be made to see if the signal across C7 is properly smoothed. If C7 was not smoothing the signal properly, a half-wave rectified (and highly distorted) version of the signal would be produced across R10.

If all was well thus far, the next step would be to use a multimeter to measure the voltage across C7 to ensure that it reflected the amplitude of the input signal. An amplified version of this signal should appear at the output of IC3. The signal across C9 is subjected to modifications by the timing circuit, and should rise relatively slowly, but decay almost immediately when the signal from the guitar is terminated. This signal is at a relatively high impedance, especially with decay time control VR2 set towards maximum resistance. Consequently, an analogue multimeter could produce slight loading on the voltage across C9, although it would probably not seriously upset the operation of the circuit. The voltage at the output of IC4 (pin 6) is at a low impedance, and should accurately reflect the signal levels across C9.

Logical Processes

When fault finding it is important to work logically through a circuit, reaching reasoned conclusions rather than jumping to conclusions. If the voltage across a resistor and a capacitor is too low, it could be the resistor that has gone short circuit, but it is just as likely to be the capacitor that is causing the problem. Come to that, the fault could be in the circuit feeding the resistor and capacitor. It might even be due to an accidental short circuit on the circuit board, or a "dry" joint. Always bear in mind it is possible to locate the part of the circuit that is faulty using voltage tests and (or) signal tracing, but some further testing will be needed in order to find the precise cause of the fault.

With linear circuits it is sometimes possible to take an educated guess as to the likely cause of the fault, using the way the equipment is behaving to provide useful clues. For instance, if an amplifier works fine apart from the fact the voltage gain is too low, the likely cause of the problem is a resistor or a capacitor in one of the negative feedback networks. If there is excessive mains "hum" and the power supply is working properly, a supply decoupling capacitor or "hum" filter capacitor is the most likely cause of the problem.

If an amplifier sounds fine at low volume settings, but produces increasing distortion levels at medium to high volume settings, it is unlikely that any preamplifier stages ahead of the volume control are at fault. These stages operate at the same level regardless of the volume control's setting. It is almost certainly the power amplifier section that is at fault, as this section is driven harder at high volume levels. The most likely cause of the problem is that the d.c. bias level of the power amplifier is too low or too high, causing clipping to occur on one set of half cycles if a certain output signal amplitude is exceeded. If the distortion occurs at all volume settings, and is much the same at any volume setting, it is likely that the fault is in the circuitry ahead of the volume control.

Where the behaviour of a circuit gives clues to the nature of the fault it is possible to "cut corners" by going straight to the likely causes of the problem. It is often possible to locate the fault very rapidly in these cases. Obviously a lot of faulty circuits will not be very obliging in this respect, and some circuits will simply fail to do anything at all. It is then a matter working your way methodically and thoroughly through the circuit until the fault is found.

Over The Limit
As pointed out previously, it is not safe to keep a unit switched on if it is drawing a high supply current. To do so would risk damaging components in the circuit, and there could even be a fire risk. There could also be some risk to anyone in the vicinity of the unit, since overheated components can and do explode. If a circuit draws a very high supply current there are two approaches to the problem. One of these is to simply use continuity checks, component testing, or other tests to locate the cause of the high current consumption with the unit switched off. It is probably best to explore this avenue before

trying the second approach. Check the obvious candidates first, such as electrolytic decoupling capacitors across the supply lines. Has a decoupling capacitor gone short circuit, or has one been connected with the wrong polarity?

If static tests do not locate the fault it may be necessary to power the circuit via a current limiting circuit. It is only fair to point out that there is no point in using this method if there is a genuine short circuit across the supply rails. With the supply rails short-circuited it is not possible to get a significant voltage across them, and no worthwhile voltage measurements can be made. With a short-circuit or very low resistance across the supply rails the fault can only be found by persisting with static tests. With a large circuit it is sometimes possible to cut the supply to various parts of the circuit. In this way it should be possible to locate the part of the circuit that is causing the overload, so that this section of the unit can then be given a close examination.

If the supply current overload is something less than a short-circuit, it may be possible to operate the unit at a reduced supply potential so that some meaningful voltage tests can be made. It has to be pointed out that this method is likely to be of little use with logic circuits, which often only function properly over a very narrow supply voltage range. The only common exceptions are circuits based on 4000 series CMOS devices, which will work over a supply voltage range of at least three to 15 volts. If a circuit normally operates at (say) 12 volts, it may function acceptably at a reduced supply potential of around three to five volts.

However, with logic circuits it is often easy to locate the faulty section of the circuit, because most of the components are integrated circuits fitted in holders. It is just a matter of unplugging the integrated circuits, one-by-one, until the high current consumption no longer occurs. The last device removed is probably the faulty component, but do not overlook the possibility of overloads on its outputs (particularly if it is some form of high current driver). This method sometimes works with linear circuits, but there are often numerous other components in a linear circuit which could be the cause of the problem. Remember to switch off before removing or replacing any integrated circuit. Fitting or removing any semiconductor with the circuit powered-up is likely to damage the device.

On The Up And Up

If you decide to go ahead with tests at reduced supply voltage, there are two basic methods of powering the circuit. One is to use a bench power supply that enables a suitably low supply voltage to be set. Ideally it should also have an adjustable current limiting circuit that can be set to limit the supply current to a suitably low level. You sometimes find that the supply current tends to rise steadily. A current limiting circuit will limit the supply current to a safe level if you fail to notice that things are going awry. Remember to disconnect the normal power source before connecting the bench supply to the circuit!

The second method is to use the normal power source, but with a series resistor added in the non-earth supply lead to the circuit. The value of the resistor must be chosen to give a maximum current flow that is approximately equal to the normal current consumption of the circuit. This is easily calculated using Ohm's Law. Suppose that the circuit is powered from a 12 volt supply and that it has a normal current consumption of about 20 milliamps (0.02 amps). Dividing the supply voltage by the current consumption gives the correct value for the series resistor, and in this example this works out at 600 ohms (12 volts divided by 0.02 amps = 600 ohms). The circuit will be providing some resistance, so it is best to choose the nearest preferred value below the calculated resistance. In this example a value of 560 ohms would therefore be used.

In practice it would probably be safe to use a somewhat lower value, giving a slightly higher supply current than normal, since the normal supply current of 20 milliamps is quite low. A value as low as 270 ohms should be satisfactory, giving about double the normal supply current, but I would be reluctant to use a resistor much lower in value than this.

Of course, the resistor must have an adequate power rating, and the dissipation in the resistor is given by multiplying the supply voltage by the current consumption. In this example this gives us 12 volts multiplied by 0.02 amps, which equals 0.24 watts. Consequently, a normal quarter or one-third watt resistor should be adequate. If a higher supply current was to be used, the power rating of the resistor would need to be higher. A supply current of 40 milliamps would require at least a half watt resistor for example.

When taking voltage measurements with a reduced supply voltage you obviously have to allow for the fact that a lower than normal supply potential is in use. A potential divider that provides a half supply voltage bias will obviously provide half the reduced supply voltage. On the other hand, the voltage difference between the base and emitter of a silicon transistor remains at about 0.65 volts, and is not affected by a reduction in the supply voltage. As always, the test results need to be carefully analyzed, with the temptation to jump to conclusions being resisted.

Summary

Do not make tests on mains powered equipment when it is plugged into the mains supply unless you are absolutely sure you know what you are doing. Do not make voltage checks on mains powered equipment that has a "live" chassis. Only make continuity checks, etc., with the unit unplugged from the mains.

Voltage tests represent a quick means of locating most types of fault, but a multimeter is required for this type of testing. Even the cheapest of analogue multimeters is much better than no multimeter at all, but a low cost digital type probably represents the best low budget option.

Remember to allow for the loading effects of the multimeter when making measurements on low current circuits, especially if you are using an analogue multimeter.

Analogue multimeters are delicate instruments - treat them with due respect.

Actual readings can be significantly different from calculated "typical" voltages anyway. It is voltage readings that are clearly incorrect that you are looking for.

Where a circuit diagram does not provide test voltages it is not usually too difficult to guesstimate them. Test voltages for integrated circuits can usually be found in the relevant data sheet.

Voltage checks will usually locate the general area of a fault, but some faults will not produce any unusual circuit voltages. In any event, further tests, such as component checks, will be needed in order to locate the precise fault.

With linear circuits, especially audio types, signal tracing will often provide the quickest means of locating the general area of a fault. Again, further tests will usually be needed in order to find the exact nature of the fault.

Do not leave a circuit switched on if it is drawing a much higher than normal supply current. Doing so could cause expensive damage, and could even be dangerous. Use static tests to locate the fault, or (where appropriate) power the circuit at reduced supply voltage.

Try to adopt a logical approach to fault finding, reaching reasoned conclusions rather than jumping to conclusions.

Chapter 3

TESTING LOGIC CIRCUITS

In some respects there is little difference in fault finding on linear and logic circuits. When checking for mechanical faults it makes no difference whether the circuit is a linear or a digital type. The procedures are exactly the same in either case. Signal tracing techniques can often be applied to both types of circuit, with a test signal being monitored at various points in the circuit, until an abnormality is found. Basic voltage test can be used with logic circuits, such as checking that the supply potential is correct, and reaching the supply pins of every integrated circuit.

Highs And Lows

There are also major differences though, and in this short chapter we will consider these in some depth, together with some simple test procedures to deal with them. One of these differences is that logic circuits often have numerous signal lines. Linear circuits mostly have one or two, plus (possibly) another in the form of a side chain. This multitude of signal lines can be problematic unless you have access to some pretty advanced test gear. However, in most cases it is still possible to locate the fault using simple test equipment, but it might take a little longer.

Certainly the most important difference is that logic circuits only deal with two signal voltages. A low voltage (logic 0) and a higher voltage (logic 1). These logic levels are often just referred to as "low" and "high" respectively. The actual voltage ranges that constitute low and high logic levels depend on the type of logic device in use, and in some cases also depend on the supply voltage.

For 4000 series CMOS devices a low logic level means a voltage of between zero and 30 percent of the supply voltage. A high logic level is from 70 to 100 percent of the supply potential. For 5 volt TTL logic devices the logic 0 voltage range is zero to 0.8 volts, and the logic 1 voltage range is two to five volts. In both cases this leaves a gap between the two logic levels, and in theory logic outputs should only pass through this zone during transitions from one logic level to the other. Outputs should never be stable and within this invalid logic level.

In practice there are occasions when an output might actually fall between the two logic levels even though the circuit is functioning correctly. This occurs where an output is driving a l.e.d. or other relatively high current load. The resultant heavy loading can pull the output into the in-between state. This is not really a "text book" way of handling things, but provided the device is only used to drive the l.e.d. (or whatever) and no logic inputs, satisfactory results should be obtained. An output that is driving logic inputs should not settle between the two valid logic levels.

Finger On The Pulse
On the face of it, an ordinary multimeter is perfectly satisfactory for testing logic circuits. You simply check each output to ensure it is at the appropriate logic level. In reality things are not as simple as this, because most logic circuits handle high speed pulse signals. If a multimeter indicates that a test point is at an illegal logic voltage, it might genuinely be between logic levels. However, it is quite likely that the test point is pulsing at high speed, and that the multimeter is actually reading some sort of average voltage. The problem is that there is no way of telling whether the multimeter is reading a static voltage, or giving some sort of average reading from a pulse signal.

Consequently, multimeters are little used when testing logic circuits. A logic probe is a much more useful piece of gear for testing digital circuits. Logic probes vary somewhat in design and the exact functions provided, but their basic action is to indicate whether the test point is pulsing, or static and at a valid logic level. Most will also indicate if the test point is static and between the valid voltage ranges. Some also give a rough indication of the mark-space ratio if the test point is pulsing. A pulse stretcher is a fairly standard feature, and this simply gives a relatively long flash from a l.e.d. indicator if a very short input pulse is detected. This ensures that very intermittent or one-off pulses that are very brief in duration do not pass unnoticed.

Logic Probe

If you are going to undertake even occasional servicing of digital circuits, a logic probe has to be regarded as an essential piece of test equipment. Ready-made logic probes are available at quite reasonable prices, and do-it-yourself versions are quite simple and inexpensive to construct. Figure 3.1 shows the circuit diagram for a simple but effective logic probe for the home constructor. It is primarily intended for use with CMOS logic circuits, but it can be switched for use with TTL types.

In common with most logic probes, it is powered from the circuit under test. A big advantage of this method is that the supply voltage of the probe automatically matches that of the test circuit. The current consumption of the probe depends on factors such as the number of l.e.d.s that are activated, the input frequency, and the supply voltage used. However, it is generally no more than about 10 milliamps, and the circuit under test should have no difficulty in supplying this.

The unit has three l.e.d.s which indicate whether the test point is at logic 0, logic 1, or pulsing. D2 is the "low" indicator, and it is driven from IC1b. The latter is one section of a dual voltage comparator, which is very much like a dual operational amplifier. One important difference is that its outputs are of the open collector variety, but in this case they have discrete load resistors (R7 and R8) which effectively convert them to conventional class A output stages. The inverting input of IC1b is driven by the input signal. The non-inverting input of IC1b is fed with the lower voltage produced by R3 to R5. This voltage is about one third of the supply voltage, and the output of IC1b goes high if the input signal goes below this level (i.e. if it is at a valid CMOS logic 0 level).

The other section of IC1 drives the "high" indicator l.e.d., D1. Its non-inverting input is fed with the input signal, and its inverting input is fed with the higher voltage produced by R3 to R5. The reference voltage fed to the inverting input is about 70 percent of the supply voltage, which is the minimum valid level for a logic 1 signal. If the input goes above this level, the output of IC1a goes high, and D1 is switched on to indicate that the input is at a valid logic 1 voltage. Under standby conditions R1 and R2 bias the input to half the supply voltage, which places it between the valid logic levels. This ensures that neither D1 or

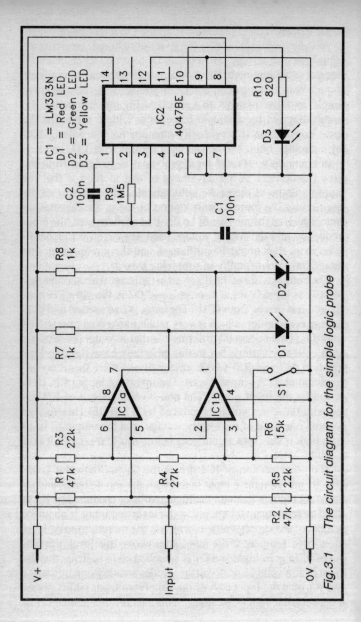

Fig.3.1   The circuit diagram for the simple logic probe

IC1 = LM393N
D1 = Red LED
D2 = Green LED
D3 = Yellow LED

D2 are switched on if the probe is applied to a test point which is "floating", which could be either a faulty output or a tristate output that is switched off.

IC2 is a CMOS 4047BE astable/monostable, which is used here as a positive edge triggered monostable. In this application it does not really matter whether it is positive or negative edge triggered. The important point is that it will be triggered by input pulses, producing a positive output pulse of about 370 milliseconds in duration. This is long enough to produce a clear "flash" from D3, even if the input pulse only lasts a micro-second.

Although the unit is primarily intended for operation with circuits based on 4000 series CMOS devices, it works quite well with many TTL circuits if S1 is closed. This reduces the reference voltages to IC1, giving a better match to TTL logic levels. Although IC2 is not TTL compatible, in practice it will trigger reliably from TTL input signals provided the input pulse duration is not extremely short. Bear in mind that 4000 series devices operating from a 5 volt supply can only operate at frequencies of up to a few megahertz, whereas most modern TTL devices can operate at frequencies around 30MHz or more.

A suitable stripboard layout for the logic probe is provided in Figure 3.2. The underside view of the board appears in Figure 3.3. The board has 34 holes by 16 copper strips. Construction of the unit is fairly straightforward, but the connections are packed quite close together on some parts of the board, making it necessary to take more care than normal to avoid accidental short circuits.

A unit of this type is normally built in the form of a hand held probe, with the input of the circuit connected to the metal prod of the probe assembly. While it is not essential to build the unit in this form, it will be easier to use if it is. It might be possible to obtain a suitable probe-style case for the unit, but if not, it is not difficult to improvise a probe assembly based on a small plastic case. The metal prod can simply be a long 6BA or metric M3 bolt, with the connection made to the bolt via a solder-tag on the inside of the case. The connections to the supply lines of the test circuit are made via insulated leads about half a metre long, terminated using either miniature crocodile clips or clip-on prods.

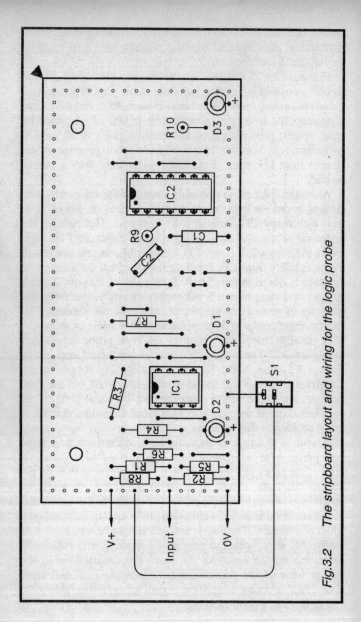

Fig.3.2   The stripboard layout and wiring for the logic probe

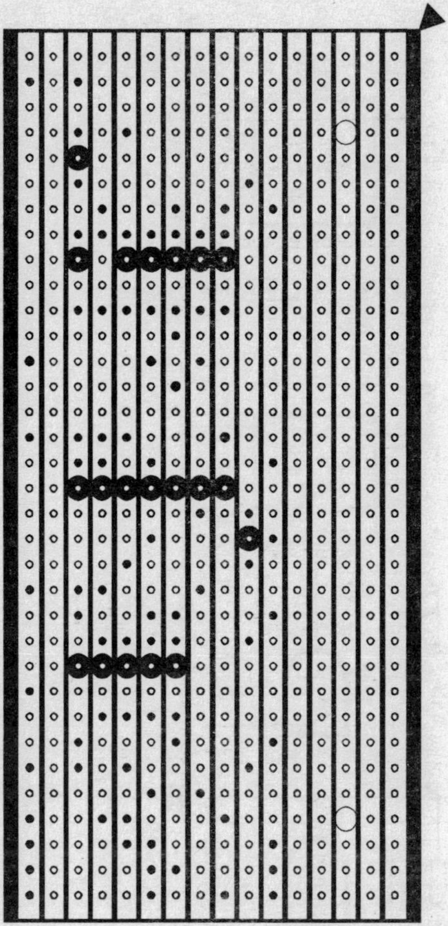

Fig.3.3   The underside view of the logic probe board

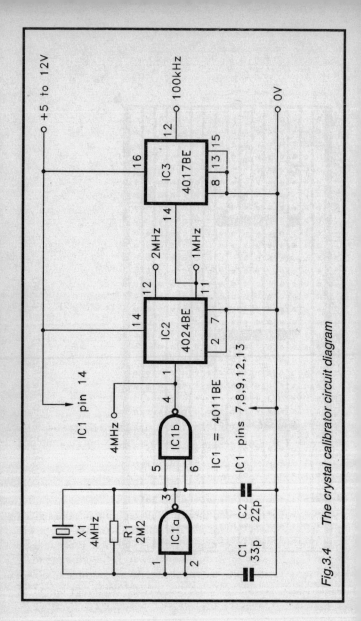

Fig.3.4   The crystal calibrator circuit diagram

98

Components for Logic Probe (Fig. 3.1)

Resistors (all 0.25 watt 5% carbon film)
R1	47k
R2	47k
R3	22k
R4	27k
R5	22k
R6	15k
R7	1k
R8	1k
R9	1M5
R10	820R

Capacitors
C1	100n ceramic
C2	100n polyester

Semiconductors
IC1	LM393N
IC2	4047BE
D1	Red LED
D2	Green LED
D3	Yellow LED

Miscellaneous
S1	s.p.s.t. min toggle

Small plastic box (see text), 0.1 inch stripboard having 34 holes by 16 copper strips, crocodile clips (2 off), 8-pin d.i.l. holder, 14-pin d.i.l. holder, wire, solder, etc.

In Use

We will assume here that the faulty logic circuit has been given the usual checks for mechanical faults, and that the power supply circuit is functioning correctly. The logic probe is used to check that each input and output is at the appropriate logic level, or (where appropriate) pulsing. As an example of how a logic probe is used, suppose that crystal calibrator circuit of Figure 3.4 is being used to provide a 100kHz signal, but no output signal appears to be present at the relevant output terminal. The circuit is basically just a 4MHz crystal oscillator followed by two divider chips which provide additional output frequencies of 2MHz, 1MHz, and 100kHz.

As with linear circuits, I prefer to start at the "beginning" and work my way through to the output of the circuit. In this case the "beginning" of the circuit is the 4MHz crystal oscillator based on IC1. The oscillator uses IC1a in a standard configuration. The purpose of IC1b is to provide buffering and amplification to ensure that the final output of the oscillator circuit is at full CMOS logic levels. IC1a is actually biased into linear operation by R1, and its output signal might be at something less than full CMOS logic levels. Consequently, it is possible that a logic probe will not indicate that a pulse signal is present at the output of IC1a (pin 3). It might indicate a static logic 0 or logic 1, but would be more likely to show an invalid logic level.

In practice the probe would probably be triggered properly by the output from IC1a, but an apparent fault condition from a logic device operated in a linear mode can not be regarded as 100 percent reliable. The more reliable test is to check for a pulse signal at the output of IC1b (pin 4). This output is at proper CMOS logic levels, and a lack of a pulse indication here indicates that the oscillator circuit is certainly not functioning correctly. Component checks, etc., would then be needed to ascertain the precise nature of the problem.

Crystal oscillators can be rather pernickety, and sometimes refuse to oscillate for no apparent reason. The problem seems to be due to differences in the crystals themselves, with some being rather reluctant to oscillate unless everything is just right. Altering the value of the input capacitor (C1) will often produce results with a lower quality crystal. If a clock oscillator fails to work for no apparent reason it is also worthwhile checking that there is no problem with the input it is driving. A damaged logic input sometimes provides a virtual short-circuit to one or other of the supply rails, effectively "clamping" the output driving it to a static logic level. The easiest way to check for this is to remove IC2 from its socket, so that there is no way IC2 can prevent the oscillator from functioning correctly.

Divide And Conquer

If a proper output signal is produced by IC1b, the problem is presumably due to a fault in one of the divider chips. IC2 is a 4024BE seven stage binary "ripple" counter. In this case it is only the output from the first and second stages that are used, and these provide output frequencies of 2MHz and 1MHz respectively. The logic probe should therefore indicate that a pulsing signal is present at these outputs (IC2 pins 12 and 11).

Particularly when using the more complex logic devices, it is quite normal for some of the inputs to be left unused. These unused inputs are not usually left "floating", but are tied to one or other of the supply rails. In this example the 4024BE has a "reset" input at pin two. When taken high this input resets all the outputs to logic 0 and holds them in that state, with any input pulses being ignored. This input serves no purpose in a free running divider application such as the present one, and it is taken low in order to permit normal operation of the divider. If there is a lack of output from IC2 it could be due to a faulty chip, or it could be the result of pin two not being connected to the 0 volt supply rail properly. The logic probe can obviously be used to check that this input is at the correct logic level.

CMOS integrated have extremely high input resistances that are usually in excess of one million megohms. Consequently, any CMOS input that is left "floating" is at the mercy of stray charges in its vicinity, and it could go to either logic state (or an in-between voltage). If a CMOS logic circuit operates erratically, the most likely explanation is that an input which should be tied to one of the supply rails has been left unconnected. Sometimes it drifts to the correct logic level and the circuit works, while at other times it drifts to the wrong logic state and the circuit grinds to a halt.

Incidentally, TTL integrated circuits have very different input stages which do not behave in the same way if left unconnected. They normally drift to the high state unless they are held at logic 0. Unused TTL inputs that must be taken low are usually connected to the 0 volt supply rail via low value resistors. Note that devices in the high speed CMOS TTL logic families have input characteristics that are more like 4000 CMOS integrated circuits than other TTL chips. Consequently, their inputs can go to either logic state if they are left "floating."

IC3 is 4017BE divide-by-ten circuit which is driven from the one megahertz output of IC2. If the 1MHz output of IC2 is pulsing, but IC3 is failing to produce an output signal, IC3 has to be the cause of the fault. Again, this device has unused inputs which are connected to the 0 volt supply rail. These are the "inhibit" input at pin 13, and the "reset" input at pin 15. The practical result of either input going high is to block the operation of the counter and hold the output at a fixed level. It would clearly be prudent to check that these pins are at the appropriate logic level before replacing IC3 with a new 4017BE.

All Together
Something like an oscillator and a divider chain is easy to test due to the serial nature of the signal path. It is just a matter of working along what is essentially a single signal path. Many logic circuits have data buses carrying eight or more bits of data at a time, plus control buses. Microprocessor based circuits also have address buses that are usually at least 16 bits wide. With the more complex logic circuits it is often helpful if the states on several lines can be monitored simultaneously. Unfortunately, this type of thing requires an expensive logic analyser, or an oscilloscope plus an expensive add-on. Few home constructors have access to this type of equipment.

This leaves little choice but to take a rather simplistic approach to testing complex logic circuits. In most cases the fault will be something quite basic, and the simplistic approach will soon locate the problem. Logic analysers and the like are more vital for circuit development than for fault finding. Although it might be helpful to know the binary pattern on a bus at a given instant, simply checking each line individually using a logic probe will often tell you what you need to know. If each line should have some form of continuous pulse train, does it actually do so? If one or more of the lines in a bus is static, it is likely that the chip generating the bus signals is faulty, or there is a mechanical fault causing the lack of signal. For example, a solder splash could be short-circuiting a data line to ground, or there could be a broken printed circuit track.

Computer add-ons that connect direct to the computer's buses have an address decoder, which invariably decodes a few control bus lines as well. The purpose of this circuit is to provide a pulse during the brief periods when the correct combination of input levels appears on the decoder's inputs. During write operations this pulse is normally used to latch data into a data latch. During read operations the pulse activates a tristate buffer which then places the data onto the computer's data bus. The data latch or tristate buffer may be built into a peripheral chip such as an analogue converter rather than being in a separate chip, but it will always be present in the circuit.

Although I normally advocate starting at the "beginning" of a circuit and working forwards, in this case it is best to start at the output and work backwards. In other words, use the logic probe to check if a pulse is produced when the computer tries to access the add-on device. If a pulse is detected at the appropriate time, and there are no extraneous pulses, it is virtually certain that the address decoder circuit is functioning correctly. The problem is therefore due to a fault in the peripheral chip which is failing to communicate with the computer's data bus.

If the pulse is not detected, or the decoder is producing extra pulses, the address decoder is at fault. You have to be slightly cautious in situations where extraneous pulses from the decoder are detected. Some of the more complex computer interface chips provide decoding for some or all of the control bus lines, and might even provide some of the address decoding. This makes fault finding difficult, and you can only be sure that the address decoder is faulty if it fails to provide any output pulses at all.

If a fault in the address decoder is suspected, first recheck for mechanical faults. If none are found, the next step is to check the integrated circuits in the address decoder circuit. Checking components, including logic integrated circuits, is covered in Chapter 4. With complex logic circuits and in the absence of advanced logic testing equipment, thoroughly checking for mechanical faults and testing the logic chips is often the most effective method of fault finding. Testing complex computer peripheral chips is probably not a practical proposition. However, if everything else in the circuit is found to be all right, it is reasonable to assume that the complex peripheral chip is faulty, and a replacement should be tried.

Chapter 4

COMPONENT TESTING

Fault finding starts with visual checks, possibly progressing to continuity testing, voltage testing, etc. It often ends with the need to determine whether or not a suspect component is the cause of all the trouble. I would warn against jumping to conclusions and assuming that a component is faulty without, if at all possible, giving at least a basic check. Some components are easily checked, and require nothing more than the cheapest of multimeters. Others are more difficult, and might require a simple test circuit to be improvised. In this chapter we will consider methods of testing a wide range of components without resorting to masses of expensive test gear.

Resistors

All the multimeters I have encountered have been equipped to check resistors having values from a few ohms to several megohms. Testing resistors should therefore be quite straightforward. However, as pointed out in Chapter 2, testing resistors in-circuit will not provide totally reliable results. In fact it will often provide very misleading results. In order to ensure an accurate reading it is necessary to temporarily disconnect one lead. When testing very high value resistors it is also essential to make sure that you are not in electrical contact with the metal parts of the test prods. Otherwise you will be adding your body's resistance in parallel with the test component. The resistance through your body can be as little as a few hundred kilohms, and would give misleading results when testing any resistors having values of a few tens of kilohms or more.

Capacitors

Capacitors are more difficult to test since most multimeters do not have capacitance ranges. In fact a small percentage of modern digital multimeters do have this facility, and in my opinion it is worth any small additional cost to obtain one of these instruments. You effectively get a multi-range capacitance meter for a few pounds, which is probably less than a tenth of the cost of buying a separate capacitance meter. Designs for do-it-yourself capacitance meters can be found in books and electronics magazines, and many of these also represent a low cost solution to capacitance measurement. Provided you have some form of capacitance measuring equipment, testing capacitors should be quite straightforward, but it can not be performed in-circuit. In fact I would recommend total removal of the suspect component from the circuit board, rather than just disconnecting one lead. Otherwise stray capacitances can give odd results, particularly when testing low value capacitors.

When testing capacitors bear in mind that the tolerance ratings of these components are generally much higher than those of resistors. Non-electrolytic capacitors are normally marked with their tolerance rating. In some cases this is in the form of a code letter, as detailed in Table 4.1. Where no tolerance rating is indicated, I generally assume a tolerance figure of 20%. For electrolytic capacitors the tolerance ratings are generally very high, with something like plus 50 percent and minus 20 percent being quite typical. Some of these components have tolerance ratings as high as plus 100 percent and minus 50 percent!

It is possible to test capacitors in a limited way using a simple multimeter. In theory a capacitor has an infinite resistance across its leads. Obviously no practical capacitor achieves this, but for non-electrolytic types the resistance should be so high as to be beyond the measuring capability of any normal multimeter. A low reading, or even one of a few megohms, almost certainly indicates that the component is faulty. With non-electrolytic capacitors there are usually no indeterminate results, and the test components either exhibit a very high resistance, or a virtual short circuit.

The short circuit is due to a damaged dielectric, resulting in the two metal plates of the component coming into electrical contact with one another. Unfortunately, the fact that a high resistance reading is obtained does not mean that a capacitor is guaranteed to be perfect. One of the leads might have become detached from its metal plate, or the value of the component could be well away from the marked value. Capacitors are not particularly expensive, so if you have no way of properly testing one that is believed to be faulty, it is probably best to go ahead and replace it.

Table 4.1

Letter	Tolerance (+/−)
F	1%
G	2%
H	2.5%
J	5%
K	10%
M	20%

Reverse Polarity

Testing electrolytic capacitors is slightly more difficult, as they are polarised, and they tend to have much lower leakage resistances. The fact that they are polarised means that the multimeter must be connected with the correct polarity. For a digital multimeter this means connecting the positive and negative test prods to the positive and negative terminals (respectively) of each test component. Testing with an analogue meter requires the connections to be the other way round, with the positive test prod connected to negative lead, and the negative test prod connected to the positive lead.

This may seem to be illogical, but you need to consider the basic arrangement used for resistance measurement using an analogue multimeter. The basic setup consists of a battery, meter movement, a fixed resistor, and a variable resistor all wired in series between the test prods (Figure 4.1). The variable resistor is adjusted to set the meter at full scale deflection with the test prods "shorted" together. Any resistance across the test prods gives reduced meter reading, and the higher the resistance, the lower the meter reading. An analogue multimeter has separate scales for the resistance ranges, as they are non-linear and reverse reading.

The salient point here is that, as can be seen from Figure 4.1, the positive test prod connects to the negative side of the battery, and the negative test prod connects to the positive battery terminal. It is therefore necessary to connect an

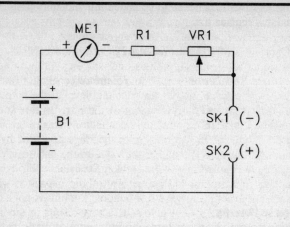

Fig.4.1   The basic arrangement used in an analogue
multimeter for resistance measurement

analogue multimeter to an electrolytic capacitor with what
appears to be the wrong polarity. If the polarity of the multimeter is incorrect, the dielectric can not function properly, and
a fairly low resistance reading will almost certainly be
obtained. There is also a slight risk of the capacitor being
damaged. Some tantalum capacitors are especially vulnerable
to voltages of the wrong polarity.

The sort of resistance reading to be expected is very much
dependent on the value and quality of the component under test.
It is quite normal for "bog standard" components having values
of 100µ or more to have leakage resistances that are measured
in kilohms rather than megohms. On the other hand, there are
superior quality electrolytic capacitors which combine high
values and high leakage resistances of a few megohms or more.
If a components list specifies a high quality electrolytic (or
tantalum) capacitor, then it is important to use a suitably high
quality capacitor. If under test the component exhibits a
relatively low leakage resistance, it should be regarded as
substandard and replaced. Most high value electrolytic

capacitors are used for supply decoupling and smoothing, and leakage resistances as low as a few tens of kilohms are unlikely to cause any problems in these applications.

Capacitors of around 0μ47 to 22μ are often used in more demanding applications, such as inter-stage coupling in audio amplifiers. The capacitor must couple the audio signal from one stage to the next, while blocking the d.c. level at the output of one stage from reaching the input of the next. In this sort of application it often requires only a minute leakage current to cause a large shift in the biasing of the stage preceded by the coupling capacitor. The higher the value of the bias resistor or resistors, the higher the required leakage resistance through the coupling capacitor. A low value electrolytic capacitor which has a leakage resistance of a few hundred kilohms is not exactly faulty, but it might not give satisfactory results in the more exacting applications. If in doubt, replace electrolytic capacitors that have slightly lower than expected leakage resistances.

When testing higher value capacitors you may notice that a low initial reading is obtained, with the reading soon increasing to a high value. This initial lack of resistance is actually due to a surge of current as the capacitor charges up, and it does not indicate a fault in the component. With a very low value capacitor this effect may not be noticeable, but with very high value components it might take several seconds for the reading to stabilise at a high value. In fact it could take several minutes, but to avoid the long wait it is best to switch to a lower range which will charge the test capacitor more rapidly.

It is possible to use this initial "blip" in the reading to roughly gauge the value of medium to high value capacitors. This is something that is easier using an analogue multimeter. The basic idea is to test some capacitors of known value to determine what sort of initial "blips" they give. Test components are then compared against the results obtained from the "standard" components. When testing components in this way remember to short-circuit their leads together first, so that they start out in a completely uncharged state. For most capacitors it will be necessary to use the highest resistance range, although it might be easier to check very high value types on one of the lower ranges.

It is not possible to make precise measurements using this method, and it is unlikely to work at all with components of less than about 47n in value. It is not usable to a worthwhile degree with some digital multimeters. However, with a suitable multimeter and capacitors of about 47n or higher in value, it shows whether or not test components are reasonably close to the correct capacitance. Capacitors (and most other components) tend to work perfectly, or to be totally useless, with few faulty components that almost work properly. If a capacitor gives plausible results when given this test, it is almost certainly fully operational.

Diodes

Diodes and rectifiers are the most simple of semiconductors, and are the easiest to test. Silicon devices such as the 1N4148, 1N914, 1N4001, etc., should exhibit a fairly low resistance in one direction, and an extremely high resistance in the opposite direction. In fact the reverse resistance should be too high to measure with an ordinary multimeter. Germanium devices such as the OA90 and OA91 also exhibit a low resistance in one direction. In fact they generally have somewhat lower forward resistances than silicon types. Their reverse resistances are also much lower than those of silicon diodes. However, the reverse resistance should still be substantially higher than the forward resistance. A germanium diode should have a reverse resistance of around 100k or more.

Many multimeters now have a range specifically for testing diodes. Most multimeters which do not have this facility can be used to check diodes using a high resistance range. The only exceptions are digital multimeters that have an inadequate test voltage to bring silicon diodes into conduction. Virtually all multimeters have either a specific diode testing facility, or use a high enough test voltage when switched to an ordinary resistance range. When using an analogue multimeter the low resistance reading should be obtained when the positive test lead is connected to the cathode (+) leadout wire, and the negative test lead is connected to the anode (−) leadout wire. Reversing the test leads should give a very high resistance reading. This method of testing is shown in Figure 4.2. If a digital multimeter is used to check diodes, the high and low readings will be

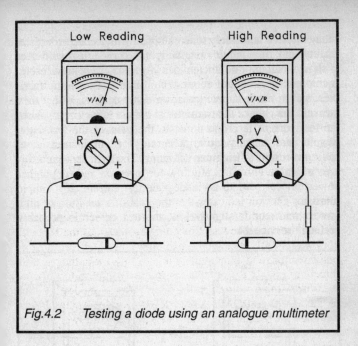

Fig.4.2   Testing a diode using an analogue multimeter

the other way round (a low resistance reading will be obtained with the positive and negative test leads connected to the diode's anode and cathode respectively).

Note that a diode does not give a genuine forward resistance, since the voltage drop through the component changes very little with variations in the forward current flow. When using an analogue multimeter to check the forward resistance there will probably be little difference in the deflection of the pointer as the meter is switched from one range to the next. Similarly, with a digital multimeter the figures displayed may change very little as the unit is switched from one range to another, with only the position of the decimal point changing. This simply reflects a characteristic of silicon diodes, and does not indicate a fault in the test components.

Transistors

Many modern multimeters are equipped with a transistor tester facility, and although this is usually quite crude, it is sufficient to show whether or not most types of transistor are serviceable. A common shortcoming of these built-in transistor tester facilities, and of many simple transistor tester designs, is that they measure the gain of the transistor at quite a low current. Also, the test current is proportional to the gain of the transistor. Results are usually quite accurate for small transistors having medium to high current gains. The indicated gain figures might be unrealistically low for low gain and (or) higher power devices, due to an inadequate test current. If a simple transistor checker indicates that the gain of a medium or high power transistor is slightly low, the test device is probably perfectly serviceable.

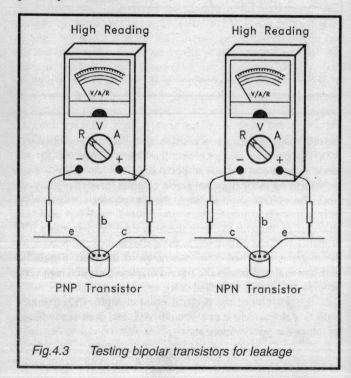

Fig.4.3   Testing bipolar transistors for leakage

It is possible to give transistors a rough check using a multi-meter set to a resistance range, provided it uses a high enough test voltage for diode checking. First the leakage resistance is checked, using the method of connection shown in Figure 4.3. This shows the correct method of connection for n.p.n. and p.n.p. transistors using an analogue multimeter. The polarity of the test prods must be reversed if you use a digital multimeter. For silicon devices the leakage resistance will usually be so high that the multimeter will be unable to measure it. Germanium transistors often have relatively low leakage resistances, but for a serviceable device the resistance reading should still be quite high.

A rough check of current gain can be made using the arrangement shown in Figure 4.4. Again, this shows the correct method of connection for both n.p.n. and p.n.p. devices. It gives the correct methods of connection for an analogue multimeter. When using a digital multimeter the test prods are, of course, connected to other way round. This setup is much the same as for leakage testing, but a resistor has been added between the base and collector terminals of the transistor. This feeds a small base current to the test device, which should result in a much greater current flow in the collector circuit. For this test it is advisable to use a fairly low resistance range so that the test device is operated at a reasonably high collector current. Worthwhile results may not be obtained if it is run at a collector current of just a few microamps. The resistor should have a value which is roughly equal to the full scale value of the range in use, which should be about 10k.

If the test transistor is functioning properly it will conduct strongly between its collector and emitter terminals, giving a resistance reading that is well short of the full scale value. The higher the gain of the transistor, the lower the resistance reading. In general the indicated resistance is around one tenth of the base feed resistance for a low gain transistor, and about one hundredth for a high gain device.

Remember that this system will not work with a digital multimeter that uses a very low test voltage. If the test voltage is too low to permit diode testing, it is also too low to drive this method of transistor checking. If the multimeter has a diode check range it will probably be possible to use this to provide a

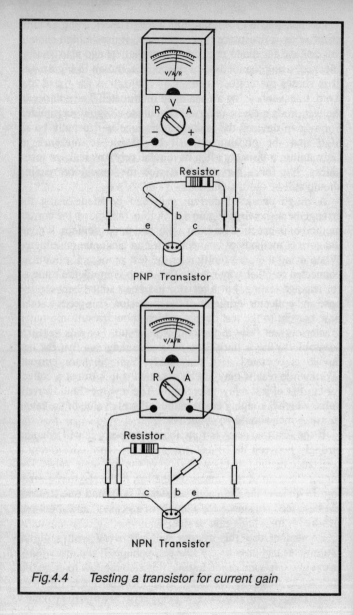

PNP Transistor

NPN Transistor

Fig.4.4   Testing a transistor for current gain

simple transistor checking facility. A little experimentation with some transistors that are functioning correctly should enable a suitable base feed resistance to be selected. It will also give an idea of the sorts of readings to be expected with various types of transistor.

As pointed out in Chapter 1, under static conditions a transistor effectively consists of two diodes connected back-to-back (see Figure 1.3). A "blown" transistor is unlikely to provide the right diode action between its base-emitter and base-collector terminals. Checking for these two diode junctions represents another simple but effective method of testing a transistor.

Inductors And Transformers

An inductor is just a piece of wire which is normally wound around a core made from a special material such as ferrite, or possibly laminated iron in the case of an inductor for low frequency use. Testing an inductor properly requires an inductance bridge, or some other form of inductance measuring equipment. Few amateur electronics enthusiasts have access to such equipment.

A very simple check that can be done quite easily is to check for a low resistance through the component. In theory an inductor has zero resistance, but clearly no practical inductor achieves this. However, for low value inductors such as r.f. chokes the resistance is usually no more than an ohm or two, and is often very much less than this. For high value r.f. chokes and very high value inductors for low frequency use the measured resistance might be much more than this. In some cases it could be a few tens of ohms, or possibly even over a hundred ohms.

If there is a low resistance through an r.f. choke it is unlikely that it is broken. The most common fault is a break in the wire or a broken connection to one of the leadout wires. High value r.f. chokes, which tend to be wound using very thin wire, are most vulnerable to this problem. This obviously gives a resistance that is too high to measure using an ordinary multimeter.

The fact that an inductor has a low resistance does not guarantee that it is in perfect working order. The problem could be that the component has the winding in more than one layer, and that there is a short-circuit from one layer to the next. This effectively removes some of the turns of wire, and substantially alters the inductance of the component. There is no simple way of checking for "shorted" turns, and it really requires some form of inductance measuring equipment.

It is possible to make a rough check if you know the correct resistance for the winding. This resistance might be stated in the retailers catalogue or the manufacturers data, or you might be able to measure the resistance of an identical component. You can then compare this resistance to the actual resistance of the suspect component. "Shorted" turns will produce a reduction in the resistance of an inductor, but the reduction may be quite small, and in some cases the normal resistance of the component will be so low as to make accurate measurements difficult. If you suspect that an inductor is faulty, it is probably best to try a replacement.

It is possible that the measured resistance of an inductor will be significantly higher than the correct figure. This usually occurs where the component is wound using a form of multi-strand wire called Litz wire. This wire is designed to give better performance at high frequencies. The strands of wire are insulated from one another, and a break in one or two of the strands effectively removes them from the inductor. The other strands of wire maintain a d.c. path through the component, but with increased resistance. An inductor that is damaged in this way should still function, but it might have a significantly altered value, and will certainly be less efficient at high frequencies. Its ability to handle high currents will also be impaired.

Comprehensively testing transformers is quite difficult, and is not really possible without a fair array of test equipment. A transformer is basically just two or more inductors wound on a single core. An a.c. signal applied to one winding (the primary) will appear as an output from the other winding or windings (the secondary or secondaries). The purpose of this is to provide a step-up or step-down in voltage. Each winding of a transformer can be given simple checks of the type used to test inductors. The most common fault is a burnt out winding or a broken wire, and in either case there will be a lack of continuity through the affected winding. When dealing with mains transformers, remember to disconnect the equipment from the mains supply before undertaking any tests.

Op Amps

Checking most linear integrated circuits is problematic, and in most cases it is really a matter of checking all the circuitry around the device. If this all seems in order, it is reasonable to assume that the integrated circuit itself is the cause of the fault. With some of the more simple devices it is possible to construct a simple test circuit, and most operational amplifiers can be checked using this method. A simple test circuit for operational amplifiers appears in Figure 4.5. If you use operational amplifiers a great deal it might be worthwhile constructing it as a permanent unit, but it is easily breadboarded as an when necessary.

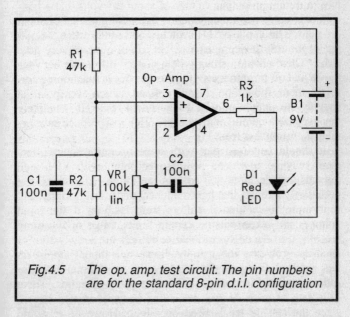

Fig.4.5   The op. amp. test circuit. The pin numbers are for the standard 8-pin d.i.l. configuration

R1 and R2 bias the non-inverting (+) input of the device to half the supply voltage, and C1 decouples any stray feedback to

117

this input. This should ensure stable operation of the test device, which is used "open-loop." VR1 provides an adjustable voltage to the inverting (–) input, and C2 decouples any stray feedback to this input. D1 is a l.e.d. indicator which enables the output state of the test device to be monitored. R3 limits the output current to about seven milliamps, although in some cases the output stage of the test device might limit the current to rather less than this. It is advisable to use a high brightness l.e.d. for D1.

With VR1 adjusted for a low voltage, the output of the test device should go high, causing D1 to light up reasonably brightly. As VR1 is adjusted for increased slider voltage, a point will be reached where the potential at the inverting input becomes higher than that at the non-inverting input. At this point the output of the test component should switch to the low state, and D1 should switch off. Some operational amplifiers have a minimum output voltage of about 2.5 volts, but a typical l.e.d. has a forward conduction threshold potential of about 1.8 volts. This can leave D1 switched on slightly when the output of the test device goes low, but it will produce very little light. There should certainly be a marked difference between the on and off brightnesses. If the test device is functioning correctly there should be a well defined switch-over point at roughly the middle of VR1's adjustment range. It is unlikely that even ultra-careful adjustment of VR1 will produce an intermediate brightness from D1.

It should be noted that with some operational amplifiers there may be a second switch-over point, with VR1 well towards one end of its adjustment range. This does not necessarily indicate that the component under test is faulty, and it is more likely that it suffers from latch-up if the input voltages are taken outside certain limits. Most of the more recently introduced operational amplifiers are largely free of latch-up problems incidentally. Some operational amplifiers lack internal compensation, and require an external compensation capacitor in order to guarantee stable operation. There little risk of such devices becoming unstable in this circuit, since the test device is used open-loop. However, it would probably be as well to add suitable compensation components when testing devices that do not have full internal frequency compensation.

SCR

A silicon controlled rectifier (SCR or thyristor) is a simple switching device which can be checked using the test circuit of Figure 4.6. Once again, this could be made as a permanent unit, but it can be easily put together on a solderless breadboard as and when it is needed.

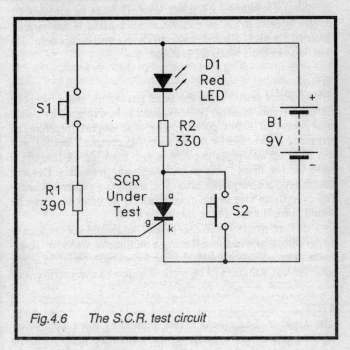

Fig.4.6   The S.C.R. test circuit

With a supply of the correct polarity an SCR can be made to conduct between its anode and cathode terminals by applying a forward bias to its gate terminal. The bias current needed in order to trigger an SCR into this conductive state varies considerably from one type to another, but is usually under 20 milliamps, and can be well under one milliamp. By operating S1 the test device can be given a forward gate bias of about 20

119

milliamps. This should switch on the test device, causing l.e.d. indicator D1 to light up.

Unlike a transistor, an SCR latches in the "on" state, and remains switched on even if the gate bias is removed. The only proviso here is that the anode current must be about 20 milliamps, or rather less than this for some modern SCRs. In this circuit the test component passes a suitably high current, and D1 should therefore remain switched on when S1 is released. An SCR can be switched off by briefly taking its anode current below the hold-on level. This can be achieved by briefly operating S2, so that the anode current is temporarily diverted through S2 and away from the test component. D1 should switch off when S2 is released.

Triacs

Triacs can be tested using the same test circuit, but a triac can handle a signal of either polarity, and can be triggered by a gate bias signal of either polarity. The triac should therefore be triggered if the polarity of the supply is reversed, but D1 will not light up unless its polarity is also reversed. A few triacs have built-in diacs in series with their gate terminals. Devices of this type are very difficult to test, and it is a matter of checking everything else in the circuit first. If no other fault can be found, a replacement triac should be tried.

Diacs are similarly difficult to test, but should not conduct in either direction when tested using a multimeter set to any resistance range, or when checked using a continuity tester. In either case the test voltage will be too low to produce triggering.

FETs

The type of f.e.t. (field effect transistor) most commonly utilized in designs for the home constructor is probably still the junction gate (Jfet) variety. Other types are also in widespread use though, such as VMOS transistors, enhancement mode MOSFETs, and power MOSFETs. We will consider all these devices here.

Care must be taken when testing f.e.t.s, as it is easy to end up with a dud device after the testing process, even if the test component worked perfectly before it was tested! Always make

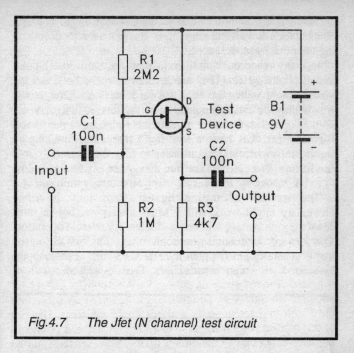

Fig.4.7   The Jfet (N channel) test circuit

quite sure that test circuits are switched off before connecting
or disconnecting test components. Be careful to keep any form
of MOSFET well away from sources of high voltage static
charges.

A Jfet can be checked using the simple test circuit of Figure
4.7. The device under test is connected to operate as a simple
source follower buffer stage, which is the equivalent of a
bipolar transistor operating in the emitter follower mode.
Unlike an emitter follower stage, where there is a voltage drop
from the input to the output, the output of this circuit will be at
a somewhat higher voltage than the input. It will be somewhere
in the region of half the supply voltage, but due to variations in
the gains of Jfets it could be up to a couple of volts either side
of this level. If possible, apply an audio signal of about one volt
peak-to-peak to the input of the circuit, and check that a good
quality signal at a similar level appears at the output of the
circuit.

This test circuit is for an N channel device, but it is easily adapted for use with P channel Jfets. It is just a matter of reversing the polarity of the supply.

In many respects, VMOS transistors are more like bipolar transistors than Jfets. They are normally switched off, and are biased into conduction by a forward bias. A characteristic which they do have in common with Jfets is that they are voltage operated, and have an extremely high input resistance. Bipolar transistors have a low input resistance, and require significant input currents in order to bias them strongly into conduction. The current flow into the gate of any f.e.t. is so low as to be impossible to measure using an ordinary multimeter.

The method of testing bipolar transistors described previously might work with VMOS transistors, but in most cases the gate voltage will be insufficient for reliable operation. The forward conduction threshold voltage for VMOS transistors is generally much higher than the 0.65 volts or thereabouts associated with bipolar transistors. The simple test circuit of

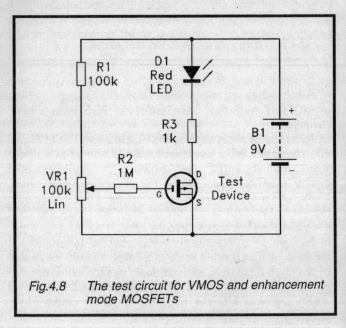

Fig.4.8   The test circuit for VMOS and enhancement mode MOSFETs

Figure 4.8 provides a more reliable method of testing VMOS transistors. This is another test circuit that can be easily breadboarded as an when it is needed.

With the slider of VR1 at the bottom of its track the test device is cut off, no significant drain current should flow, and D1 is switched off. If VR1 is adjusted for a steadily increasing wiper voltage a point should soon be reached where the test transistor begins to switch on, and D1 starts to visibly glow. Taking VR1's wiper voltage slightly above this level should result in the test device conducting strongly, and VR1 lighting up brightly.

Power MOSFETs can be tested using the same test circuit, but note that manufacturers of these components recommend that a short gate lead should be used in order to avoid instability and possible damage to the test device. Enhancement mode MOSFETs can also be tested using the same test circuit. P channel VMOS transistors and MOSFETs are relatively rare, but they do exist. They can be tested using this circuit provided the supply polarity and the polarity of D1 are both reversed. It is obviously necessary to observe the usual handling precautions when testing any MOS transistors, including VMOS devices.

Switches

These are the most simple of components electrically, but due to their mechanical nature they are probably more prone to failure than most other components. They can obviously be checked using some form of continuity tester, and should not be at all difficult for even a complete beginner to test. However, an important point to bear in mind is that switches sometimes have intermittent faults. It is a good idea to repeat the test procedure two or three times. This greatly increases the chances of spotting an intermittent fault.

Also bear in mind that a lack of continuity between the appropriate pair of tags is not the only fault that can occur. It is possible (although admittedly rare) for a switch to produce a connection between two tags that should not be connected. It is therefore advisable to connect the continuity tester between the appropriate two tags and then adjust the switch through its full number of positions a few times to see if continuity is only indicated with the switch at the correct setting.

Switches that have numerous tags are often the cause of mistakes in the wiring due to the constructor misinterpreting which tag is which. Before wiring up a switch, especially if it is a type you are not familiar with, it is a good idea to check it with a continuity tester to ensure that you are interpreting the tag arrangement correctly.

Logic I.C.s

The basic function of most logic integrated circuits is to produce a certain output state (or set of output states) for a given set of input levels. Most logic devices can therefore be tested by simply feeding in different binary patterns at their inputs and checking for the correct output state or states. It is usually quite easy to improvise a test circuit on a solderless breadboard, but if you use a lot of logic devices it is probably worthwhile building up a simple tester. Figure 4.9 shows the circuit diagram for a simple but effective tester for 4000 series CMOS devices. It is also suitable for use with high speed CMOS TTL integrated circuits. The static logic outputs and l.e.d. indicators are also usable with 74LS TTL integrated circuits, and other modern TTL devices, but the clock outputs can not be guaranteed to drive non-CMOS inputs correctly.

SK1 to SK4 provide four outputs at logic 1, and SK5 to SK8 provide four outputs at logic 0. On the face of it there would be no problems if the current limiting resistors (R1 to R4 and R6 to R9) were omitted. In the "real world" there is a likelihood of an occasional accident, with an output of a test device being accidentally connected to one of the tester's static outputs. Without the current limiting resistors this would result in an output being short-circuited to one of the supply rails, which could damage the test component.

SK9 to SK12 give access to four l.e.d. indicators, each of which has its own current limiting resistor (R11 to R14). The l.e.d. current is quite low, and it is essential to use high brightness l.e.d.s. The type intended for operation at low currents of about two milliamps is ideal. A l.e.d. is switched on by a high logic level, and is switched off if it is driven from a low logic

124

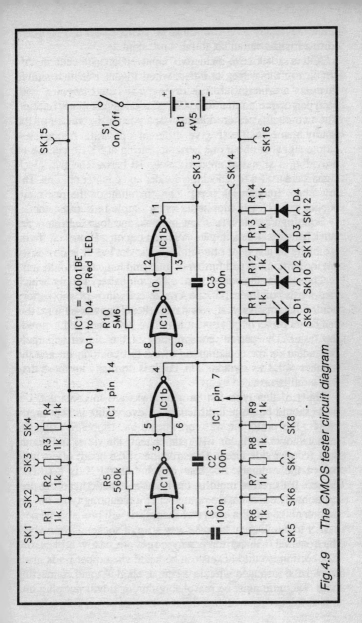

Fig.4.9   The CMOS tester circuit diagram

125

level. Obviously a l.e.d. will also be switched off if it is driven from a tristate output set to the "off" state.

IC1 is a 4001BE quad two input NOR gate, but in this circuit each gate has its inputs wired together so that simple inverters are produced. The inverters are used in pairs, with each pair operating in a basic CMOS astable (oscillator) circuit. The two oscillators are identical apart from the values of the timing resistors. These give different operating frequencies, with a signal at about one hertz appearing at SK13, and SK14 providing a signal at approximately 10 hertz. The two clock signals are useful for checking divider and counter circuits. The low clock frequencies permit the operation of the test component to be clearly monitored using simple l.e.d. indicators.

Four high outputs, four low outputs, and four indicators are sufficient to test most logic integrated circuits. However, if you are likely to test a lot of complex logic devices it is obviously not too difficult to add further outputs and indicators to the unit.

The circuit is powered from a 4.5 volt battery supply, which can consist of three HP7 (AA) size cells in a plastic battery holder. Alternatively, if you have a bench power supply, this can be set for an output potential of five volts and used to power the tester. The current consumption of the circuit is largely dependent on the consumption of the test component, and the number of l.e.d.s switched on, but it is normally no more than a few milliamps.

Units of this type can be a bit awkward to construct, but there should be no real difficulties if everything is kept pretty basic. The prototype was constructed on stripboard using the layout shown in Figure 4.10 (component side view) and Figure 4.11 (copper side view). Construction of the board offers little out of the ordinary, but bear in mind that IC1 is a CMOS device. It therefore requires the usual anti-static handling precautions. The sockets are printed circuit mounting types having a pitch of 2.54 millimetres (0.1 inches). It will probably be necessary to purchase a 24 or 32 way strip of sockets, from which the required 13 and three way strips are easily broken off. Connections to the sockets can be made via jumper leads made from 1/0.6 insulated wire, or a similar single-strand connecting wire. The wire must be reasonably thin or it will not plug into the sockets.

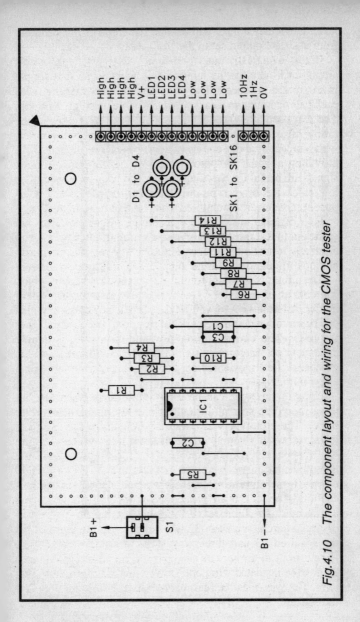

High
High
High
High
V+
LED1
LED2
LED3
LED4
Low
Low
Low
Low

10Hz
1Hz
0V

D1 to D4

SK1 to SK16

R14
R13
R11
R9
R8
R7
R6

C1
C3

R4
R3
R2

R10

R1

IC1

C2

R5

B1+ — S1

B1−

Fig.4.10 The component layout and wiring for the CMOS tester

127

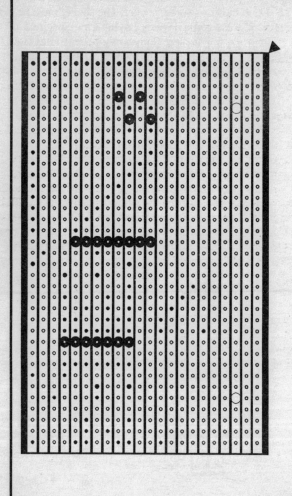

Fig.4.11 The underside view of the CMOS tester board

It is obviously essential to have some means of connecting the tester to the device under test. One way of doing this is to use a longer piece of stripboard that will accommodate a 28 or 32 way ZIF (zero insertion force) socket. The socket must be a type intended for use with devices having row spacings of either 0.3 inches or 0.6 inches. Some only accept integrated circuits which have 0.6 inch spacing, which is fine for something like an EPROM programmer, but is of little use in this application where the test devices will mostly have 0.3 inch pin spacing. Two rows of sockets are soldered to the board to permit connections to be easily made to the socket. Do not forget to add breaks in the copper strips at the appropriate points to isolate the socket from the main circuit.

On the prototype tester I used the alternative method of fixing the circuit board onto a small piece of particle board, together with a small solderless breadboard. One of the smaller solderless breadboards is likely to be a little cheaper than a ZIF socket, and it facilitates easy connection to CMOS integrated circuits of any size. Its only drawback is that it is slightly more awkward to remove devices after testing, and due care must be taken to avoid buckling any of the pins.

Components for CMOS Logic Tester (Fig. 4.9)

Resistors (all 0.25 watt 5% carbon film)

R1 to R4	
R6 to R9	1k (12 off)
R11 to R14	
R5	560k
R10	5M6

Capacitors

C1	100n ceramic
C2	100n polyester
C3	100n polyester

Semiconductors

IC1	4001BE
D1 to D4	Red LEDs (4 off)

Miscellaneous

B1	4V5 (3 × HP7 size cells in holder)
S1	s.p.s.t. min toggle
SK1 to SK16	2.54mm pitch printed circuit mounting sockets

0.1 inch matrix stripboard measuring 35 holes by 22 copper strips, 14-pin d.i.l. holder, battery connector (PP3 type), ZIF socket or small solderless breadboard (see text), single core insulated wire for jumper leads, wire, solder, etc.

In Use

In order to use the tester you really need to know the basic actions of the devices you wish to test, together with full details of their pin functions. In some cases the circuit description for the project that uses them might provide all the information you need to know. The larger electronic component catalogues are another source of useful information, as are the various logic device data books that are available. Unless you have access to some basic data on the devices you will wish to test, and you also have a basic understanding of logic principles, the tester is likely to be of limited value to you.

When using the unit always remember to make sure that it is switched off before connecting or disconnecting a test device. With multi-stage devices such as gate packages it is best to check one section at a time, rather than trying to check all the sections at once. It is not really necessary to check every possible combination of input states for gates which have four or more inputs, and it could be quite time consuming to do so. Some rationalisation will usually speed things up, but still give reliable results.

For example, with a four input NOR gate the output is high if all four inputs are low, but is low for any other set of input states. The first test is to set all four inputs low, and then monitor the output using one of the l.e.d. indicators to check that it is high. It is then a matter of taking each input high, in turn, to ensure that each one is capable of taking the output low. This checks only five input patterns rather than the full sixteen that are possible, but if the test device passes this test it is highly unlikely that it is in any way faulty.

For a device such a binary divider, one of the low frequency oscillators is used to provide the device with a clock signal to divide. For instance, suppose you wish to test a CMOS 4024BE seven stage binary counter, as used in the crystal calibrator circuit described in chapter three (Figure 3.4).

Pinout details for the 4024BE are provided in Figure 4.12.

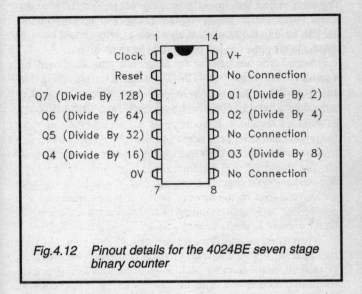

Fig.4.12   Pinout details for the 4024BE seven stage binary counter

First the positive and 0 volt supplies of the tester are connected to pins 14 and seven respectively. The only control input of the 4024BE is the "reset" input at pin two, which is initially taken low in order to enable normal operation of the device. The clock input is at pin one, and this could be fed with either the one hertz or 10 hertz signals from the tester. With seven stages of binary division the 4024BE provides a division rate of 128 from its final stage. Using a one hertz signal would give a very low final output frequency, making the test procedure rather "long winded." In this case the 10 hertz clock signal would therefore be a better choice.

Although the 4024BE has seven outputs, it is not really necessary to have seven l.e.d.s to simultaneously monitor all the outputs in order to test this component. It is just a matter of using one of the l.e.d.s to check that the output from the first stage is providing an output frequency of about five hertz. Then the output of the second stage is checked, and this should provide a squarewave at about 2.5 hertz. This process is repeated for subsequent stages, checking that each output frequency is half that from the previous stage. Finally, pin two is taken high, and all seven outputs are checked again. With the 4024BE held in the reset state all seven outputs should be low, and the input pulses at pin one should have no affect.

Provided you understand its basic function, it should be possible to test virtually any CMOS integrated circuit using this unit. With the more complex devices remember to check that each control input ("inhibit", "reset", "set", etc.) is functioning correctly.

Notes

Please Note

Babani Radio, Electronics and Computer books should be available from all good Booksellers, Radio Component Dealers and Mail Order Companies.

However, should you experience difficulty in obtaining any title in your area, then please write directly to the Publisher enclosing payment to cover the cost of the book plus adequate postage.

If you would like a complete catalogue of our entire range of Radio, Electronics and Computer Books then please send a Stamped Addressed Envelope to:

BERNARD BABANI (publishing) LTD
THE GRAMPIANS
SHEPHERDS BUSH ROAD
LONDON W6 7NF
ENGLAND